ZODIAC

STOCKTON-ON-TEES

Edited by Lynsey Hawkins

First published in Great Britain in 2002 by
YOUNG WRITERS
Remus House,
Coltsfoot Drive,
Peterborough, PE2 9JX
Telephone (01733) 890066

HB ISBN 0 75433 644 1
SB ISBN 0 75433 645 X

FOREWORD

Young Writers was established in 1991 with the aim of promoting creative writing in children, to make reading and writing poetry fun.

Once again, this year proved to be a tremendous success with over 41,000 entries received nationwide.

The Zodiac competition has shown us the high standard of work and effort that children are capable of today. The competition has given us a vivid insight into the thoughts and experiences of today's younger generation. It is a reflection of the enthusiasm and creativity that teachers have injected into their pupils, and it shines clearly within this anthology.

The task of selecting poems was a difficult one, but nevertheless, an enjoyable experience. We hope you are as pleased with the final selection in *Zodiac Stockton-On-Tees* as we are.

CONTENTS

Jessica Jones	18
Joanne Dunn	18
Aaron McKevitt	19
Rebecca Lingard	19
Catherine Conlon	20
Matthew Carson	20
Sarah Gaunt	21
Rachael Mazzey	21
Rachel Moran	22
Christopher Hogarth	22
Terence Johnson	23
James Davies	23
Samantha Nolan	24
Rachel Robson	24
Tom Bell	24
Craig Mott	25
Jordan Millward	25
Louise Johnstone	26
Jade McKevitt	26
Maria Kowal	27
Liam Curran	27
Abbie Rayner	28
Poppy Williams	28
Daniel Walker	29
Daniel Durham	29

Red House School

Amy Catterick	30
Toby Andrews	31
Paul Johnston	32
Jennifer Chaytor	33
John Harris	34
Jake Richardson	35
Glen Rayment	36
Jennifer Murphy	37
Tom Jones	38
Nigel Parkash	39
Paul Stubley	40

St Patrick's RC Comprehensive School

Matt Lockwood	71
Clare Thompson	71
Matthew McGee	72
Gareth Cox	72
Rhiannon Beckett	73
Andrew Farndale	73
Philip Smith	74
David Golden	74
Faye McDearmid	75
Damon Towes	76
Leah Iveson	77
James Adams	78
Hayley Jobson	78
Jamie Robson	79
Michelle Carter	80
Claire Sturdy	81
Matthew Hall	82
Rebecca Newbold	82
Samantha Remmer	83
Rob Illingworth	83
Michael Wass	84
Rebecca Latham	84
Jennifer Leighton	85
Stacey Gavaghan	85
Jamie Green	86
Philip Turnham	87
Andrew Hardy	88
James Henderson	88
Lauren Barclay	89
Racheal Moy	89
Leah Kelly	90
Adam Porteous	90
Amanda White	91
Lyndsey Walker	91
Stuart Blackburn	92
Stephanie Burns	92
Jay Kelly	93

Rebecca Oliver	93
Jenna Sharp	94
Katie Fairbairn	94
Danny Wood	95
Michael Cartwright	95
Lee Robinson	96
Caitlin Harrison	96
Lee Jones	97
Stephen Powls	97
Eleanor Gaynor	98
Alex Dorrington	98
Clare Peacock	99
Kayleigh Hope	100
Shaun Smith	100
Amy Green	101
Laura Payne	101
Katie Poppleton	102
Hellen Frost	102
Daniel Flynn	103
Matthew Brown	103
Leanne Trotter	104
Rebecca Quigley	104
Claire Horner	105
Jennie McPhee	105
Jenny Macaulay	106
Daniel Kelly	107
Brett Spence	108
Daniel O'Riordan	108
Rachael Postgate	109
Jennifer Heatley	109
Rachel Kelly	110
Christopher Raymond	111
Beverley Marwood	112
Martin Heward	113
Steven Liggett	114
Kathryn Buckland	115
Sammi Brocardo	116

Westlands School

The Poems

TYRANNOSAURUS REX

T eeth as sharp as a pencil
Y ou'd have to be lucky to survive the crush
R un, run as fast as you can
A nd closer and closer. He is very fast!
N ever even climb a tree
N ever ever stop and rest
O r he will crush you like a bug
S hake and shake all you can you'll never escape
A t last you've hidden somewhere
U nder a tree
R un he can see you
U nder the tree, he is about to crush
S ad that, he has hurt his foot.

R ex is a fearsome dinosaur
E specially when he is hungry
X -tra dinner he longs to have.

Paul Butterfield (11)
Our Lady & St Bede's School

ELEPHANTS

E veryone loves elephants
L iving peacefully not harming anyone
E ating juicy, green leaves
P laying like children, walking slowly
H uge, big feet and trunks like ice cream cones
A pproaching big feet, crushing stones
N othing can stop them from carrying on
T railing along, lumbering over grasslands
S leepily in safe herds at night.

Charlotte Muckian (11)
Our Lady & St Bede's School

IN THE DARK

In the dark I heard a creak,
Then I heard someone speak.
I got out of bed, turned on the light,
There was nothing there, but I still got a fright.
In the darkness under my bed,
Something stirred and it wasn't my ted.
I heard it creeping out,
Should I shout?
I looked at the creature fearfully,
I murmured tearfully.
'Don't hurt me,' I said.
'I won't' came the reply, 'but I'd like to live under your bed.'
'Are you a friendly creature?' I enquired.
'Always,' it whispered, 'unless I get tired.'
'In that case you can stay.'
'Thank you,' it said, 'I promise I won't get in the way.'

Amy Wright (11)
Our Lady & St Bede's School

FUNKY MONKEYS

Down in the middle of the jungle,
Funky monkeys disco dancing,
Wild and lively singing,
Do you really like it?
It is really swinging.
Monkey, monkey, monkey, monkeys are at play,
Munching, crunching every day.
'Hey, giz a banana.'
'No you can't have me I'm too yellow for you!'

Michaela Harris (12)
Our Lady & St Bede's School

PHANTOM FAZACALTY

When Colonel Fazacalty died,
Over the eggs that had just fried,
He landed nose first in the butter dish,
Well Phantom Fazacalty floated away,
Past the tree and across the bay,
Floated Phantom Fazacalty.

Well when Phantom Fazacalty floated away,
Past the tree and across the bay,
The pesky poltergeist that had pestered,
Colonel Fazacalty rejoiced 'Finally,' he said,
'I've seen him dead!'
Now while the poltergeist was talking,
He was flying up and up 'Oh no!' he said.
'Now that Colonel Fazacalty's dead! I'm off to heaven
And I can't enjoy my house!'

Joshua Rowntree (11)
Our Lady & St Bede's School

A MONSTER IN THE JUNGLE

A monster in the jungle swinging through the trees
Laughing and smiling and scratching his fleas.
He's as quiet as a mouse with claws like a cheetah,
Only one difference - he's not a meat eater.
He gobbles up leaves, juicy and green.
Now in his area there's no trees to be seen.
Also he's partial to a bit of rice pud.
He enjoys potato fritters with glasses of mud!
He's been known to eat ice cream but it's a bit hard to find.
Could you give him some?
Would you be so kind?

Joseph Syson (11)
Our Lady & St Bede's School

WHAT HAVE WE DONE?

The streets are polluted,
Covered in gum,
Sometimes I wonder,
What have we done?
Graffiti on walls,
Painting on shops.
There's litter almost everywhere.
Packets and slops,
What kind of people would want to do this?
Wrappers, chewy, bottles of fizz.
Under clear blue skies and the morning sun.
I look at the Earth and think,
What have we done?
Only people with good habits amiss,
Would throw away wrappers and bottles like this.
There's ruined rivers with cans and boxes,
A poor habitat for badgers and foxes.
The pollution inhibits the river's run,
What I'd like to know is
What have we done?

Heather Langan (11)
Our Lady & St Bede's School

THE JUNGLE

I was walking through the jungle
Suddenly I saw a lion
Gazing into my eyes.

I was walking through the jungle
Suddenly I saw a bear
What a surprise!

I was walking through the jungle
Suddenly I saw a snake
Giving soft hisses and cries.

I was walking through the jungle
Suddenly all the animals were around me.
My fear I could not disguise!

Polly Trotter (11)
Our Lady & St Bede's School

AUTUMN TIMES

Autumn's here and the leaves are falling,
Picking them up is very, very boring.
School is still on
And we are still mourning!

Days are getting shorter,
Nights are coming faster,
And the neighbour next door
Definitely has a ghetto blaster!

Trees are bare,
It's a horrible sight.
Where's the sun gone?
We need some light!

In the end though
It's alright.
Bonfire Night
Hallowe'en.
We give people
A very big fright!

Jonathan Everett (13)
Our Lady & St Bede's School

MY ROOM

Open the door and you will find,
A room of the very small kind.
It has a small window and bed,
And that's what I always said.

Open the door and you will find,
A room of the very small kind.
It has a small wardrobe and desk,
And that's where I do my homework, it's the best!

Open the door and you will find,
A room of the very small kind,
It has a small table and chair,
And that's when I open the window to get some fresh air.

Open the door and you will find,
A room of the very small kind.
It's sometimes tidy and sometimes a state,
And that's when I go call for my mate.

Sean Dunn (12)
Our Lady & St Bede's School

RABBITS

Rabbits are funny creatures,
Nibbling on carrots,
Chomping on grass,
Running over meadows in the cool evenings.
Basking in sunshine on long summer days.
Longing for the morning when it is still night.
Rabbits are very fluffy,
Cuddly too.
I bet you agree with me and love them too!

Lucy Smith (12)
Our Lady & St Bede's School

A MADE UP CREATURE

I live unseen far, far beneath the abysmal sea.
Even if you look hard you can't see me.
I live in the dark deep sea
With other creatures less friendly than me.

I do not bite, bark or scream.
Just swim around as happy as can be.
No friends or family, birds or bees,
Just me in the deep abysmal sea.

Unknown am I
As the years go by.
I change my disguise
To cause surprise.
But I'm kind and good
Causing no trouble - no creature should!

Francesca Small (11)
Our Lady & St Bede's School

WHO AM I?

I move as quietly as a mouse,
I'm small, but bigger than a louse.
My eyes are big and brown and clear.
I have big ears so I can hear.
My nose will twitch all day and night,
My fur is long, it's brown and white.
Living in the garden doesn't seem much,
But I'm quite safe in my cosy hutch.
Gnawing on everything is my habit,
Have you guessed?
Why, I'm Flopsy the rabbit!

Frances Allinson (11)
Our Lady & St Bede's School

SEASONS

Spring is for birds
and of their tweet.
Spring is for new birth,
spring is so neat.

Summer is for ice cream
summer is for breaks
summer is for holidays
swimming in the lakes.

Autumn is for leaves
falling to the ground.
Autumn is for conkers
falling in a mound.

Winter is for Christmas
and when presents overflow.
Ice is on the window ledge
and lovely fluffy snow.

John Flynn (12)
Our Lady & St Bede's School

TOO MUCH SILENCE

S   ilence in the park, no one
I   n sight I feel alone, I feel a fright.
L   ingering sounds clatter and shatter.
E   verybody's gone home, I'm all alone.
N   oises here, noises there, noises everywhere.
C   lothing is rustling shoes.
E   choing the trees are waving, I'm going home
     I'm all alone.

Natalie Ward (13)
Our Lady & St Bede's School

WHICH SEASON IS THIS?

Dark, stormy, thunder clouds,
Raining throughout the night,
In the morning a mild contrast,
Sunny, though not too bright.

Even though the sun shines
The air still feels quite cold.
Its rays make little difference
If I may be so bold.

The wind can be fresh and bracing,
You cannot plan ahead,
Your day out could be ruined
You might wish you'd stayed in bed.

Which season is this, are you wondering?
Seasons in England are a guessing game.
Autumn, winter, summer, spring,
All four of them are much the same.

Nicholas Chapman (12)
Our Lady & St Bede's School

HAUNTED

H   aunted is my house in the middle of the night
A   nd sometimes gives me a fright
U   nder the table, under my bed
N   o more I said
T   ell me I'm asleep
E   veryone, don't make a peep
D   on't wake up in the middle of the night.

Danielle Broadbent (11)
Our Lady & St Bede's School

ZOMBIES

Z ombies rise from the grave,
O n the full moon they rise,
M ysterious creatures,
B rain eating,
I ntestine chewing,
E vil dead,
S atan brings them.

Steven Jenkins (11)
Our Lady & St Bede's School

TROLL

Sluggish and slow, but very strong,
Stupid and tall, carries a club.
A troll will eat anything that gets in its way,
Talking in grunts, utters few words.
Only three types - River, Forest and Mountain.
Around twelve foot tall, towering other creatures.
A thing you would not want to mess with,
Unless you have a death wish.

Tom Roberts (11)
Our Lady & St Bede's School

SHARK

S ee the shark swimming in the deep ocean.
H unting in the ocean, can't wait for his tea.
A lways keeping an eye out for his prey.
R ising to the shimmering light at the surface.
K nowing the right time to attack his victim.

Peter Todd (11)
Our Lady & St Bede's School

MONSTER ALERT

M agnificent monster
O n a log, crouching
N ot mean or cunning, actually he looks kind
S ort of friendly in a monster way
T rusting, but not timid
E choing along a forest trail, he moves
R oaring, but not fiercely, as if he knows something that I don't.

Nathaniel Aaron (11)
Our Lady & St Bede's School

MURDERING MONSTERS

On the mountains lives a monster.
We all fear he's going to attack.
He scares the death into us.
He comes down from the mountains each year.
He's a horrifying beast,
We all are his feast.

Jordan Malpass (11)
Our Lady & St Bede's Schoo

AUTUMN

A utumn is a season,
U sing different colours of red, gold, yellow and orange,
T o brighten up the world.
U ndergoing a process that will take all year.
M usic is played by the howling wind.
N ow it will soon be winter.

Peter Southern (12)
Our Lady & St Bede's School

SCHOOL

The big building where we learn,
That place where we go early in the morning.
Where we get shouted at by moody teachers.

Teachers walking, talking around you,
And then you work all day long trying to please,
But still your work is no good.

Break time, people playing and talking to their friends,
Footballs flying everywhere, just missing heads.
Bell goes, next lesson about to begin,
More working to do,
But dinner is coming soon.

Bell has gone, it's time to eat.
Around a table, eating my dinner.
Talking to my friends,
Teachers eating in the corner, telling us to be quiet.

Get marked in, go to your lesson,
Work, work, work, is all we do.
Then another lesson, more work, work, work.

Home time at last, lessons finished,
We are dismissed.
Bet we will be back tomorrow for more -
Work, work, work!

Jenny Nicholson (11)
Our Lady & St Bede's School

HOMEWORK! OH, HOMEWORK!

I hate you! You stink!
I wish I could drown you in my sink.
If only you were a bomb
I would explode you to bits.

Homework! Oh, homework!
You're last in my list.
I cannot see
Why you even exist?
Oh! Homework, oh! Homework!

Sarah Bright (13)
Our Lady & St Bede's School

DARK AND LONELY

Out in the valley in the middle of nowhere
Lonely in its silence
No one goes there anymore only a mouse,
Rat or the odd grizzly bear.

No one will come any further than town.
No one can hear you scream.
No one will see if you cry or even
If you're mean.

Out in the valley
Stands this lonely home.
A new family might one day occupy these dark rooms,
In which shadows do now daily.

No one will come any further than town.
No one can hear you scream.
No one will see you if you cry or even
If you're mean.

Now we will leave
Lonely place
And it's dark, dark rooms.
Maybe one day we will return to this quietness like tombs.

Amy Lamph (12)
Our Lady & St Bede's School

SNOW

Over a carpet of pure white snow,
The busy people to and fro.
Not noticing the dirty street,
The leaves beneath their trudging feet.

Suddenly it seems to turn,
Those silly people never learn.
All that's left is a slushy mess,
To get upon your Sunday best.

All this magic seems to go,
We'll never again see that snow.
And yet when we wake next morn,
There's snow upon the garden lawn.

When they were asleep it came flying.
Now still and lifeless it was lying.
Ready to face another day,
Another day to be swept away.

Rhiannon Ellis (12)
Our Lady & St Bede's School

TYRANNOSAURUS REX

A huge lizard,
a terrible beast,
without doubt it's looking for a feast.
A meat eater, a carnivore,
who can tell what he's waiting for?
Vicious, ambitious, full of war,
he is after blood and gore.
Lurks in the dark, in the park,
. . . Jurassic Park!

James Paterson (11)
Our Lady & St Bede's School

AROUND THE WORLD WITH MY AUNTIE DORIS

In the forest
With my auntie Doris
Picking conkers,
She was bonkers.

On a desert plain
Doris was so vain.
For a mirror she would look
Searching in the muck.

On the ice
Eating biscuits that were nice.
Sailing round and round
By a penguin we were found.

On the train home
We passed a man on a mobile phone.
Back among the Britons,
Pulling on our woollen mittens.

Emma Cumiskey (12)
Our Lady & St Bede's School

SWEET SHOP

Everywhere you look you see sweets,
Chocolate liquorice, ten pence mixes,
Jelly sweets, lots of treats,
Children's heaven especially that seven,
Gobstoppers and the Mouthpoppers,
Fireballs, chocolate walls,
Chewing gum everyone come,
Sugar lumps, powder plumps,
But the best of all is the fizzy Flumps.

Ellie Stephenson (11)
Our Lady & St Bede's School

WINTER

Winter is coming
December's begun
The days are longer
There is no sun!

Children are out playing
Building snowmen in the snow
Children are happy
The sun is no more!

The weather is much colder
Children are getting older
Day by day
The days fade away!

Claire Scott (12)
Our Lady & St Bede's School

THEY JUST IGNORE ME

All the children ignore me,
When I try to be their friend.
They do not hurt or call me names,
They just ignore me.

I don't think they talk about me,
I don't think they know my name.
They run away and play their games,
I'm always by myself.

I don't know what's wrong with me,
And why I even exist.
To the eyes of the children,
I am part of the mist.

Sarah Varey (12)
Our Lady & St Bede's School

HALLOWS EVE

Ghosts and ghouls
Wicked witches
Frankenstein's monster
Falls in ditches.

Vampires, pumpkins
Zombies galore,
There can't be much more.

Devils, skeletons and bats
Evil witches
With their cats.

Knock, knock, who's there?
Is there anything else out there?

Anna Knibbs (12)
Our Lady & St Bede's School

THE FIRST DAY OF SPRING

The sky is clear,
No clouds to be seen.
The grass is changing,
From yellow to green.

The flowers are reappearing,
And the birds can
Be seen singing.

The weather is getting better,
So now I don't need
My big, fluffy sweater.

Mark Jones (13)
Our Lady & St Bede's School

AUTUMN

As the orange and brown leaves fall,
From the old trees that stand so tall.
My foot makes a crunch as I walk,
The leaves that are falling whisper and talk.

Conkering is a pastime enjoyed by all,
They are knocked down with sticks or when
                              they're ready they'll fall.
They love to be rid of their prickly skin
When they do, again the process will begin.

Hallowe'en night is upon us once more,
Witches and wizards, they'll knock at your door.
The children roam all night long,
'The grass is green' is their Hallowe'en song.

Jessica Jones (13)
Our Lady & St Bede's School

A SNOWY DAY AT SCHOOL

Overnight the snow has turned into one long slope
On five school yard steps,
No one can sit on the playground swings,
Buried deep under drifts of snow,
In still-falling snow.
Perching crows shake trees of flakes
In still-falling snow.
Classroom radiant with snow light.
Your face reflects each turning page.
The whole classroom seems to freeze
    In still-falling snow.

Joanne Dunn (14)
Our Lady & St Bede's School

THE DRAGON

The dragon, swift as a snake,
His claws, like a five-pronged rake.
Wings, strong as a log,
Tail, a swirly fog.
Fire, strong enough to burn anything,
His teeth, sharp as a sword,
The people around him, gifts they bring,
The dragon, is sharp like a sword.

As the sunset falls,
He roars his call,
His home, is a cave,
Warm, cosy and safe.
Even though his death awaits,
He still manages a burning flame of anger.

Aaron McKevitt (11)
Our Lady & St Bede's School

MY ROOM

Yellow, pink and purple walls,
And lovely little mirrorballs.
On the floor lay a purple bed,
And a silver futon bed.
On the desk is a yellow lamp and a red TV.
Very noticeable for everyone to see.
On the TV is a crucifix
And a remote control that my dad's going to fix.
On the wall in front of the wardrobe
Is a pale green robe.

Rebecca Lingard (11)
Our Lady & St Bede's School

WHITE HORSES

When the white horses come to play
It will always be my favourite day
Mares and stallions, oh what a joy
Hamish is my favourite boy.

He comes to me and tickles my toes,
Splashing around wetting my clothes.
Out he goes to the blue marine
Where has he gone, my darling dream?

Yes, the white horses are the waves of the sea.
Leaving mark on the sand and enjoying being free.
The tides have come on this summer day.
One day, one day I will have to pay.

Catherine Conlon (12)
Our Lady & St Bede's School

ALL YEAR LONG

January is the month of snow,
February is winter's final show.
March is the start of the spring season,
April has showers for no apparent reason.
May is the month before the season of sun,
June is the time, for going to the beach, and having some fun!

July is the middle of the year,
August's when hot spells begin to occur.
September is the month for going back to school,
October's when the weather starts to get cruel.
November is when snow first starts to fall,
and December, is for Christmas and a good one to all.

Matthew Carson (12)
Our Lady & St Bede's School

MONKEY BUSINESS!

Monkeys are funky as they swing through the trees,
They seem to say: 'Give me a banana please!'
They curl their tails into all kinds of shapes,
They're fond of fruit - especially grapes.
Their antics entertain us at the zoo,
They're always doing something new.
The babies cling to their mother's back,
Watchful for others who might attack!
Grinning slyly they hold out a paw,
They sidle towards the cage door.
Watch out, they are very, very cunning,
If you open the door, they'll never stop running.
Then you would face an angry man
Who has to catch them (if he can)!

Sarah Gaunt (11)
Our Lady & St Bede's School

PETS

Pets are lovely and furry,
Some live in hutches,
Some live in tanks,
Others are around us all the time.

Some pets creep around in the dark,
Others play games as though they are at the park.

Sometimes I wonder what it's like to be a pet,
Without a plan of how life is set,
I wonder what it's like to be trapped in a cage.

I think they might want to be free!

Rachael Mazzey (11)
Our Lady & St Bede's School

ELEPHANT

There is an elephant
Called Nelly-phant!

She is grey and black
With a huge, strong back.

She has a large appetite
And comes out at night.

She has a long trunk,
Full of water she's drunk.

She roams over plains,
Then returns home again.

She's proud and she's wise
She's as tall as the skies.

Rachel Moran (12)
Our Lady & St Bede's School

LOOKING THROUGH THE WINDOW

When I look out of the window
And what can I see?
I can see a bird, looking at me.

When I look out of the window
And what can I see?
I can see rain splashing at me.

When I look out of the window
And what can I see?
I can see the moon looking down at me . . .

Christopher Hogarth (14)
Our Lady & St Bede's School

THE ALIENS ARE HERE

Quick, run, hide! The aliens are here.
They are coming closer and closer.

We need to protect ourselves, they may be hostile.
Get the police, get the army!
Let us hide in our houses.

Quick, run, hide! The aliens are here.
They are coming closer and closer.
What do I hear them saying?
They're here to be our friends!
They're not here to frighten us.
What a relief!

Terence Johnson (11)
Our Lady & St Bede's School

THE SCISSOR-TAIL

In the middle of the sea,
Under a huge rock,
Buried deep in the sand,
Is the huge Scissor-tail.
He waits to jump out
And snap his scissor-like tail,
At the sea creatures who swim innocently by.

He slices seaweed with his sharp, lethal tail.
He slices up the unsuspecting fish.
He is a dangerous presence,
Lurking at the very bottom of the sea.

James Davies (11)
Our Lady & St Bede's School

FLIPPER THE DOLPHIN

Flipper the Dolphin?
Oh yes, I know him well.
He is so clever.
He helps rescue people in danger.
Sometimes he even helps the police.
He has lots of friends - people as well as animals.
He is a great favourite with the children.
I *love* the Flipper films
They are such fun to watch.

Samantha Nolan (11)
Our Lady & St Bede's School

IN MY GARDEN

In my garden the flowers do grow,
In my garden the snails and worms go slow.
In my garden the wasps and bees collect nectar,
Then I watch them go.
Down in the garden among the flower beds,
The flies go buzz,
They drive and fly between them.
I like my garden, it's big and long,
It's just like me!

Rachel Robson (11)
Our Lady & St Bede's School

FRED'S HEAD

There once lived a man called Fred
Who was always in his shed.
He was working on an experiment,
To make his head fat and red.

He finally made his head go fat,
But it also started to grow wings like a bat.
He tried to get his head back into shape,
But he couldn't, so he had to wear a cape.

Tom Bell (11)
Our Lady & St Bede's School

MY FRIEND BUNGLE

I was walking through the jungle
When I saw my friend Bungle.
Bungle is a big, friendly bear,
The last thing he wants to do is scare you away.
I've known Bungle for years
I've never seen him in tears.
He's always cheerful and bright
He'll never give you a fright.
He is a companion forever,
I love him beyond treasure.

Craig Mott (11)
Our Lady & St Bede's School

MY DAD

My dad is called Dan
He lives in a van,
He is very smelly,
He has a big beer belly.
He also has a bald patch,
And he went to a footie match.
I saw him eating out of a bin,
Thank goodness, I don't live with him!

Jordan Millward (11)
Our Lady & St Bede's School

MY ROOM

Dolphins, dolphins, everywhere,
even a dolphin teddy bear.
Dolphins on the bedcover,
dolphins on the curtain.
I love dolphins that's for certain.
TV on my chest of drawers,
and my puppy dog with big paws.
Phone next to my bed,
'You're not having a phone' Dad said.
On my desk is a picture of my cousin
and probably another dozen.
On the floor is a dolphin bed,
'This is lovely' I said.

Louise Johnstone (11)
Our Lady & St Bede's School

HERE COMES THE DOLPHIN

Look at the baby blue dolphin
Splashing gaily beside his mother.
His smooth, silky side glitters silver,
As the water flows over it.

Does he know how beautiful he is?
Does he know how lucky he is to have such freedom?

I see him leaping in the warm, blue water,
And I envy him.

Jade McKevitt (11)
Our Lady & St Bede's School

WHAT HAS MAN DONE?

Once the air was fresh and clean,
It's been polluted now it seems.
Once trees grew everywhere,
Now only stumps and logs lie there.
Once the streams were fine and fair,
Now they are dead and bare.
Once the animals were all free,
Now they're caged for men to see.

We explore the stars, the moon and sun,
But back on Earth,
We think, 'What has Man done?'

Maria Kowal (11)
Our Lady & St Bede's School

ALL ALONE

Silence in the house,
me all alone.
Then all I hear is a ring on my phone.
I go to my bedroom still all alone,
My mum should be back soon, I hope so!
Then all I hear is a huge loud *bang*
All I do is look around . . .
Nobody here, except me, all on my own.

Poor Me!

Liam Curran (13)
Our Lady & St Bede's School

THE MONSTER

Deep down under the ground
There lived a monster that heard every sound.
When people walked over his spot,
He would object a lot.
Then he'd get up and poke his head through.
'I'd go away quickly if I was you!'
Then he'd go down and try to sleep.
Sometimes he would even start to weep.
It can be sad living under the ground,
Even a monster sometimes wants someone else around.

Abbie Rayner (12)
Our Lady & St Bede's School

BIRDS FLY SO HIGH

Birds fly so high,
fluttering in the sky.
While down below,
the lamp posts glow.
There's people dancing,
people glancing,
people far below.
The birds watch them go,
as they fly to their nest
for a rest.

Poppy Williams (11)
Our Lady & St Bede's School

MY ROOM

My girlfriend called Jessie
Keeps my room messy.
It's 'orrible in its way
It grows messier day by day.
It's never clean,
That's why Mum gets mean.
My dad doesn't care,
At least he can't be unfair.
My sisters don't help,
Mum just came up 'Yelp.'

Daniel Walker (11)
Our Lady & St Bede's School

THE SNAKE

Snakes, snakes!
As long as rakes
Slithering and sliming
Double-quick timing.
Shredding their skin
Sleek and thin.
Poisonous venom to avoid
We must not make a snake annoyed!
Treat him always with respect and care,
If he moves towards you - *beware!*

Daniel Durham (11)
Our Lady & St Bede's School

PANTHER

Think of its glittering eyes
Sparkling in the moonlight;
The swish of its liquorice tail
As it leaps into a tree
And with a careless hop
Reaches the top
Making the birds fly free.

Think of its smooth fur
Silky and shiny in the sunlight;
The imprint of its great paw
Deep in the soil,
Like a teddy bear hand.

Think of its muscular structure
Rippling under its stretched skin
At break of day;
Its careful walk,
Head held high and proud
Paws soundless on the ground.

Forget its beetle-black staring eyes,
Its snake-like tail
Swaying timelessly
To hypnotise a defenceless creature,
Its bright white fangs,
The hide and sneak
Of this carnivore,
Predator.

Amy Catterick (13)
Red House School

THE CAR JOURNEY

Being bored is annoying, isn't it?
You start talking to yourself, you don't think straight.
Other than that, all that happens is . . .
The slightly numbing feeling sets in.
You stare at something and you can't stop.
Finally you say to yourself 'Why am I doing this?'
Because I have nothing to do . . .
Yup . . .
I've got to do something!
I'll read a book. (Am I that bored?)
But on the other hand . . .
I've read that book before.
I'll wait for something to happen . . .
What was that on the road?
Nothing . . .
Back to the waiting . . .
Still here . . .
Mum, 'Look at me, I'm bored!'
Yup, definitely still here . . .
Anytime now . . .
Look at me, I'm getting desperate . . .
Like staring at a blank page . . .
Just kill me now.
Huh, parents are so inconsiderate, I could be dying here!
I'm getting sleepy, I'm that bored.
Zzzzzzzzzzzz
'We're here!'

Toby Andrews (11)
Red House School

A Unicorn In Barbed Wire

The day was so bright
that England beat Australia at cricket;
the World Trade Center rebuilt itself
and everyone had an international party.

At Alderly Edge a unicorn got its horn stuck in barbed wire
and neighed.

An elderly cop turned his siren to full volume,
because a siren can't be heard when a unicorn neighs;
and some kids blamed the storyteller.
Why did he make up the unicorn?

Towards evening the man in the moon paid full attention
and the stars couldn't wait to come out,
but still the unicorn neighed.

Then along came Goths riding their skateboards,
accompanied by a pair of wire-cutters,
and a dignified sales manager took off his bowler hat,
took the wire-cutters . . . and advanced to the fence.

Their way led over two rivers
before the unicorn came in sight.
It was an event like the moon landing, an event like a solar eclipse.
The unicorn stood still; the Goths jumped off their skateboards;
the stars turned out their lights; the wind stopped blowing.
Then the man reached out the cutters.

It was a 'snip' linking one dimension with another;
a 'snip' like the cutting of a red ribbon at the opening of a museum.
It loosened the wire;
the unicorn untangled its horn and stood free.
Silence . . .

The unicorn trotted alongside its rescuers,
to the deafening music
of its own celebration.

Paul Johnston (12)
Red House School

CAT

Think of the way the cat sleeps
Curled in a ball
Ready to switch on his purr
If you stroke his fur
Which shines in the light from the fire.
Think of the way he strolls,
Stretching his long legs,
Swinging his lean tail with ease.
Think of him watching you
From the trees.

Forget the way he hooks his claws
In the chairs and pulls,
The way he scares the birds,
Stares at you with narrowed eyes
Following your every move.

Jennifer Chaytor (14)
Red House School

A SHEEP DOWN THE HILL

The day was so bright
that tigers broke out of the zoo,
all elephants lost weight,
and lorries on the M1 bounced on their tyres.

At Dilford a sheep fell down a hill and baaad.

Athletes stormed off the athletics track opposite
because athletes can't practise when a sheep baaas,
and Farmer Jones was traipsing round the streets cursing Farmer Fred:
'You just let a sheep fall down a hill and leave it there!
That, I'm telling you, is preposterous.'

Towards evening, even the flowers started to droop
and the grass at the bottom of the hill grew thorns;
but still the sheep baaad.

Then along came some boys, armed with a sturdy hank of rope,
and a hippy laid on the hill . . .
his banjo . . .
he laid aside his banjo and took up the rope.

Their way led down the rough hill to the bottom where the sheep
waited.
It was a quest like no other; a quest like the conquering of Scafell Pike.
The sheep lay silent; the boys pulled like Mick McManus;
and the hippy heaved like Hercules.
The wind blew viciously;
grasshoppers hopped with curiosity; everything went still,
and the hippy stretched out his hand.

It was a hand combining two worlds, life with death;
it was a hand offering everything;
it caught the sheep by its springy wool.

And then they heaved back
to the deafening symphony of the sheep's baaaing.

John Harris (12)
Red House School

FRENCH BULLDOG

Smile at the warm way
He can mould to your shape
When he's on your lap,
In his soft, black velvet coat
With the bright white patch on his chest.

Smile at his squashed up nose
Flat as a pig's, at his bat-like ears
And tail-less rear;
At his fangs that flicker in the light
And glow in the dark,
At his bark.

Flinch at his sharp nails
Which can strip your skin
With one smooth scratch,
At his heavy breathing
Like an old man trying to catch his breath.

Jake Richardson (13)
Red House School

A PEACOCK IN THE COAL MINE

The day was so bright
that the Twin Towers moulded back into shape,
Bin Laden took a day off, and no one went to work.

At Branton a peacock fell into a coal mine and yowled.

Children playing nearby ran with fear
because there was a monster groaning from the mine,
and mothers were cursing the miners:
'You let a peacock fall in the mine;
then you left it there,
and this has been going on for hours.'

Towards evening the stars pierced the sky's dark cloak
and the whole town was fast asleep, as quiet as a mouse,
but still the peacock yowled.

Then along came some boys, and got in the mine cart,
and a miner left on the ground
a pick-axe . . .
he laid it aside and rode with them.

Their way led deep into the earth,
to the coal-pile where the peacock waited.
It was a ride from an Indiana Jones film,
A roller coaster through darkness.
The peacock fell silent; the boys were frozen
and a piece of coal fell.
The walls breathed loudly; insects crawled under rocks;
the heavens stood still, and a miner stretched out his hand.

It was a rescuer's hand, a hand of freedom.
It was a hand joining everything together;
it caught the peacock by its scrawny neck.

And then they rode back
to the music of an immense fanfare of the peacock's squawking . . .

Glen Rayment (13)
Red House School

AN EXTENSION TO A DREAM

I'm in a place out of the city,
Where the surroundings are calm and tranquil,
There is trilling water coming from a purling stream,
It's like an extension to a dream.

The clouds are brushing the hilltops,
And the birds are sailing to the ground.
It's so unique I wish I could stay,
It feels like I'm in a land from far away.

As I stand on top of a hill,
It's like I'm on top of the world.
I look at the phenomenal views around me,
It's as if I've been miraculously lifted from equality.

The landscape is extraordinarily captivating,
And the fields are like a patchwork quilt.
In the distance I can see a house girded with flowers,
I could gaze at this spectacular scenery for numerous hours.

As night falls the wonderful features begin to fade
And the day transforms into night,
And as the sun sinks behind the hills like a falling feather,
I know that I will remember this day for ever.

Jennifer Murphy (13)
Red House School

AN EAGLE DOWN THE CHIMNEY

The day was so bright
that poverty was destroyed,
the ozone hole was repaired
and an Englishman won Wimbledon.

At Keswick a great eagle fell down a chimney and squawked.

Police officers jumped in their cars and left
because policemen can't work when an eagle squawks,
and an old-age pensioner complained:
'Officer, why don't you do something?
that bird's been there since ten.'
But all the officers had gone.

Towards evening the Earth had stopped moving
just so, the sun could get a good view;
and the stars came out early to join the spectators,
but still the eagle squawked.

Then along came three boys
and a businessman with his Mercedes.
They made a ladder with rope and climbed onto the roof.

Their way led across the tiles and up to the top of a chimney.
It was a trek like Captain Scott's to the North Pole.
The eagle fell silent; the rope ladder was slowly lowered
and was hooked around the eagle's body.
The wind stopped;
the bell-ringers missed the six o'clock chimes;
the ropes pulled up
and the businessman's hand reached out.

It was a hand like the hands of God and Adam as they made contact;
it caught the eagle under its belly and pulled it out of the chimney.

Then the eagle flapped its great wings
and screeched in celebration.

Tom Jones (12)
Red House School

JIM WHO HAD A BIG GRIN

There was a boy whose name was Jim,
All he did was grin and grin.
He liked to grin and act the fool,
Annoying the teachers at his school.

Out of school was just the same,
He grinned like mad and was a pain.
When his friends wanted him to chat,
He grinned at them like a Cheshire cat.

He found his grin stuck one day,
Then his friends ran away.
Lion's teeth gripped him hard,
No grin could save him his life was scarred.

He regretted the day he made a grin,
And swore to never do this sin.
Instead he found another joke,
And that was to trick the other folk.

Poor Jim is now a naughty boy,
His teachers do not like this ploy.
He's in trouble day by day,
Never allowed to go out to play.

Nigel Parkash (11)
Red House School

THE DAY THAT WENT WRONG

At first the day was peaceful, as peaceful as could be,
But it shaped up rather badly, as you will swiftly see.

We were to drive to Timbuktu
And then come back via Bakerloo,
But even though it started well
It soon turned into a traveller's hell.

We were to leave the house at ten,
But Dad was trapped in the *rabbit pen!*
And at the car, Mum couldn't get in
All sorts of dilemmas were about to begin.

Just as we neared the end of the drive
The baby whinged and Bobby cried
'Oh stop the car, oh turn round Mummy
We have forgotten the baby's dummy!'

As soon as we all got on the road
Dad found out that Jim had stowed
The family's dog and cat and *fish*
Inside his favourite *cooking dish.*

When we got a mile from home
Claire started to wail and moan
She said we had forgotten Molly
Certainly her favourite dolly.

And only then were we to find
The car had left one wheel behind
And as the journey was so bumpy
We all went home feeling very grumpy.

Everything had just gone wrong
We surely couldn't have carried on,
And as we sat, hearts fuil of sorrow
We decided to try again tomorrow.

Paul Stubley (11)
Red House School

VICKY THE THUMBSUCKER

There once was a girl called Vicky,
You'd think her thumb was always sticky.
For she always sucked her thumb,
Her mum would smack her bum.
All Vicky did was suck her thumb and sit,
Her mum would nearly have a fit.
Every day she would watch TV,
She'd suck her thumb constantly.
Her mum eventually got so mad,
She had to call Vicky's blooming dad.
Her dad told her off,
He said he'd chop the thumb off.
She begged and she begged,
But her dad shook his head.
Before she knew it,
He had already done it.
The blood was all over the bed,
The next day she was on the floor dead.
So the next time you suck your thumb,
Remember Vicky.
It could happen to you!

Oliver Whelan (11)
Red House School

QUEENIE

I remember when I went to see her,
My heart was filled with joy,
A little pony standing there,
I knew she was the one.

When I knew that she was mine,
How happy that made me feel,
I couldn't wait for her to be at my home,
I knew that then I would never be alone.

She was finally here,
The dream pony I had always wanted.
She was white as snow,
Such a cute face,
As I looked into her eyes I began to cry.

Tears of happiness ran down my face,
I knew that my heart would never be as full again.

We went through years together,
Maybe not winning, but having fun.
I remember the 'games' when she did run,
Faster and faster shining like the sun.

Everyone loved her, everyone wanted her,
But I would never leave her,
Because I loved her the most.

I remember going home one day finding her there,
Not moving,
Not breathing,
It was her time to go.

The memories I'll always have,
The times we shared, I'll never forget!
I miss her so much! Why did she die, I do not know?
Why did she have to go?

Sophie Moss (14)
Red House School

A FLOWER FOR THE SOUL

A flower for the soul starts in the brown, muddy soil,
As a seed in the ground,
It roots till it finds the point to stop,
Then it begins to grow upwards,
Slowly, gradually towards the light,
Till a little, green shoot appears.

This little, green shoot then grows up high,
Till some people think it reaches the sky,
A bud then appears,
On the top of the stem,
Which looks like a round, plump beetroot.

This red bud then opens up wide,
It gazes up to the sky,
It is in red segments,
It looks amazing.

My friend comes along,
And plucks it from the ground,
And takes it to the graveyard,
A tribute to the dead.

Andrew Tate (11)
Red House School

A CAT IN THE TREE

The day was so bright
that flowers came alive,
the sky was electric
and fairy tales were true.

In Carlton a kitten was stuck in a tree and cried.

Old women left for town,
because the kitten's cries gave them a headache,
and a grumpy, fat farmer was complaining to his wife:
'A cat gets up a tree and can't get down,
but the neighbours . . .
well, they just can't be bothered to get up and help.'

Towards evening the sky's fairy lights came on
and illuminated the tree,
but still the kitten cried.

Then along came two boys,
and made an unlikely ladder out of wood and string
and a thin, elderly man, leaning heavily on his stick
laid his stick on the bank . . .
and climbed with the boys.
Their climb led them up to the top most branch
to the twig where the kitten clung.
It was a climb like the first ascent of Everest;
or one of Jason's voyages.
The kitten fell quiet; the boys held their breath with silent delight;
the tree's leaves parted; the whole world was still
watching and waiting as the man held out his hat.

It was a hat which linked sorrow with joy; hate with love;
the cat climbed inside and sat still.

Then they started their descent
to the slow rhythm of the cat's thankful purrs.

Lucy Apps (12)
Red House School

THE LAKE

As I look out over the cold, shimmering lake,
I see reflections of bright stars glowing in the dark water.
I feel scared, alone . . .

In the night's air mosquitoes buzz around me,
I feel like running from this deserted place!
I feel scared, alone . . .

The fish in the lake look up at me and stare,
I think they're trying to warn me.
Their pleading eyes look yellow in the murky lake.
I feel scared, alone . . .

My heart beats fast as the moon shines brightly on the barren ground,
The birds in the trees are like gargoyles shadowing my every move.
I feel scared, alone . . .

I feel scared, scared of the darkness,
I feel alone, alone in the mist . . .

Thomas Naylor (11)
Red House School

THE CAT IN THE TREE

The day was so bright
that every river glistened in the sun,
flowers chorused in delight and the swallows soared into the sky.

In Durham a cat got stuck in a tree and yowled.

Rats and mice scurried away from the terror
because how could they think of nesting with a sound like that?
And the major stomped and shouted:
'Dear God, just listen to that racket,
I blame the Government for this!'

Towards evening, the moon glimmered sadly
and the leaves on the trees swirled and rattled
but still the cat yowled.

Then along came some children
who had borrowed their dad's ladder,
and a glamorous lady left on the moonlit grass
a handbag . . .
she put aside her handbag and climbed with them.

Their way led across snapping twigs
to the branch where the cat waited.
It was a voyage like the first journey into space,
a voyage like that of the mighty Titanic.
The cat stopped silent; the children stood still;
the stars twinkled and winked and the owls glided softly in search
                                                    of prey.
The world held its breath, as the lady reached out a slender hand.

It was like uniting two nations together, sadness with happiness;
it was a link joining everything together;
it caught the cat by the scruff of the neck.

And then they sailed down
to the immense crescendo of the cat's miaowing.

Ciara Hennessy (12)
Red House School

TOO MANY SWEETS!

There was once a very silly girl,
Who loved to feast on caramel twirl,
Chocolate and sherbet dips,
Barley sugar and Walnut Whips.
When she saw things in the shop,
Straight away in she would pop.
To her sweet tooth she would give in,
Confectionery would always win.
Lollipops, candysticks oh she loved them all,
But the ones she loved the most were very very small,
She did in fact crave for creamy Cadbury's Roses,
For when she went to the shop she bought them in large doses.
She literally ate them by the ton,
But by the time that she was ten the dentist pulled out all her teeth
So she was left with none.
The caution that should be taken, the message put across,
Is that too many sweets, too much junk, results in tooth loss.

Jennifer Phillips (12)
Red House School

A Sheep In The Stream

The day was so bright
that school was abolished
that the world was at peace,
and wars were a thing of the past.

In Yorkshire a sheep fell in a stream and baaad.

People enjoying a picnic ran from the former tranquil bank,
walked away because of the racket,
and a man complained that nothing was being done to help the sheep.

Towards evening the moon awoke in shock at the noise,
and the water in the stream became grey with death,
but still the sheep baaad.

Then along came some children
and made their way into the stream,
and along came a man
who left some shoes on the bank
and waded with them.

Their way led across a grey expanse
to a rock where the sheep was precariously balanced.
It was an event like the floods in Mozambique;
an event like swimming the Channel.
The sheep went quiet;
the water grew calm;
the trees leaned away from them.
Nothing moved
except the man who stretched out his arms.

These two arms made the difference between life and death;
these arms were the sheep's saviour;
they broke the sheep's fall.

And then they waded back
to the rising chorus of the sheep's baaing.

Mark Ritchie (12)
Red House School

SEA PARADOX

The coral reef hides many luxurious sanctuaries
for its frivolous inhabitants.

It's a whole different world; yet it's still on the same planet.
Whole countries in the deep blue sea have yet to be discovered.
As only one tenth of this blue planet has been uncovered.

The unimaginable has been imagined in the sea,
many people have been given miracles by it;
yet it has also taken lives away.

It may be vast, it may be blue, but it will always be a part of my life.
Whether I'm swimming in my blue planet or not.

The contrasting colours, fish and coral all so very beautiful
in their own unique way.
Its unhappened, unexplained, frightful, relaxing, freshness,
                                        intrigues me.

Lorna Routledge (13)
Red House School

A GOOSE STUCK IN WIRE MESH

The day was so bright
that the hens laid fresh, perfect eggs,
the bluebells jingled a little tune,
and the Eiffel Tower was painted gold in sunlight.

At Farmer John's farm a goose got its neck stuck in wire mesh and
honked.

Snooty men reading newspapers left the benches they sat on,
because a person can't concentrate when a goose honks,
and an old, hag-like lady was moaning to Farmer John himself:
'First you let your goose get stuck in that unimaginable situation,
and then you leave it honking all day.'

Towards sunset the bluebells drooped
and fellow geese pecked at the goose's tail feathers
until its bottom was bare, but still the goose honked.

Then along came some boys
who hopped over Farmer John's gate,
and a tramp left outside Farmer John's farm, a hat . . .
he laid his stolen hat aside and joined them on their journey.

Their way led through a smelly hen house
to the goose pen and the wire mesh that entrapped the goose.
It was a journey like the discovery of an abandoned mine;
a journey through a cat flap.
The goose fell silent; the boys crawled through the opening
the hen house creaked unsurely; hens moved cautiously out of reach;
the clouds stood still, and the tramp reached out.

It was a hand linking two similar individuals,
the tramp with the goose;
it was a hand joining two friends for life;
it caught the goose by its neck.

And then they crawled back
to the concerto of the goose's quacking.

Laura Han (12)
Red House School

AT THE END OF MY BED

At the end of my bed, at night there lies
A vampire bat that swoops and flies
There happens to be a ferocious tiger
And a great, big, enormous, hairy spider.

There even is a ghost, which wails
So I hide under my sheet as my courage fails
A Cyclops lives down by my feet
Both of which he's tried to eat.

Normally I would not dare
To go and see what else is there,
But now I'm going to have a try
Hoping that I will not die.

I'm going into this terrible lair,
And now I see there's nothing there.

Sam Powell (11)
Red House School

A Cat In A Broken Fence

The day was so bright
that the grass glistened like a carpet of emeralds,
cotton wool clouds pranced around the sky
and flowers sang and danced in the warm summer wind.

In Yarm a fat cat lay stuck in a hole in a fence and yowled.

A man passing by turned,
while his mad dog yapped at the humiliated cat,
and people in cars watched and laughed as the cat frantically struggled.

Towards evening clouds gathered as if to pay homage to the night
and moths danced furiously around the glow of the lamp light,
but still the cat yowled.

Then along came some girls
who wanted to help the distressed animal,
and a man across the road left a newspaper . . .
he laid aside his paper and helped them.

Their way led across a moonlit road
to the fence where the cat waited.
It was an event like a scene from a movie,
an event like a page from an action-packed novel.
The cat fell silent; the girls stood mesmerised
and one of them started to pull.
The squirrels scurried into the safety of the tree;
the owl left his perch on the fence; the world waited
and the rescuers all began to pull.

It was a hand like vital oxygen for a baby's first breath;
disaster and safety;
it was a hand making the difference between success and failure;
it caught the cat by its long, bushy tail.

And then they walked back
to the orchestration of the cat's continuous miaowing.

Rochelle Bates (12)
Red House School

ROBIN

Smile at his brilliant scarlet breast
Boldly standing out
In the cold snow
And bleak weather;
At his blunt beak which darts
In quick, sharp movements,
At his wings
Which flutter as he sings,
At his tennis ball body
And pipe-cleaner legs.

Frown at his small belligerence;
At his readiness to fight
For his right to territory;
At the way he will push
Even other robins from his bush.

Alexander Orr (13)
Red House School

A CALF DOWN THE MOUNTAIN

The day was so bright
that children's ice creams melted; cottage windows flew open
and lakes turned bright yellow with rays from the sun.

At Ambleside campsite a calf fell down the mountain and mooed.

Families moved their tents to another field
because they couldn't sleep through the noise,
and a snooty old man was cursing the manager:
'You saw a calf fall down the mountain and left him
and this if you please has been going on since last night.'

Towards evening the clouds cowered in the sky
and the grass at the bottom of the mountain withered underfoot,
but still the calf mooed.

Then along came two small boys with fishing nets
and a great plan taking shape in their heads.
The roaring of a Hell's Angel drowned out the sound;
he clonked over to the boys and bent an ear to their plan.

Their way led across a field of white, woolly ants
towards a steep drop leading down to a wall of stone,
jagged, like the awaiting mouth of a great white shark.
It was a voyage of courage; it was the retrieval task of the Falkland
                                                                    Islands;
it was Desert Storm without the sand.
The grass was like a worn out carpet beneath their feet.
The calf fell silent; the flies buzzed around them like military jets;
the boys eyes peered over the wall as the Hell's Angel reached out.

It was a hand reaching for the first apple on the tree;
it was boy to man; girl to woman; it was life in a grasp.
It caught the calf by the neck and pulled.

The ascent of the worn out carpet began
to the bleating tune of the mother's cry
as she stood above them on top of Everest.

Faye Emmerton (12)
Red House School

OCTOPUS

Think of the faded light pink of its flesh
Which shines like shimmering silk,
As it ripples in the water,
Of its eight languid legs
Which swirl and twirl on the tide
Floating wide
Like a double-jointed acrobat
Changing its shape as it swims.

Forget its piercing black eye
Which searches out its prey;
The way the deadly suckers hold
And the legs unfold
And squeeze
Until the victim sighs and dies.

Claire Warwick (13)
Red House School

ALICE

The girl who ate too much.

There was a girl named Alice,
She wouldn't fit in a palace,
She ate too much,
It ruined her touch.

Her mother said,
That girl'll be dead,
By the time she eats another pie,
She surely is going to die.

Chocolate, biscuits anything really,
Alice loved them oh so dearly,
She couldn't fit through a door,
She had to slide across the floor!

Fayrouz Omar (11)
Red House School

THE BATTLE

That Saturday in sunny May when
I was struck with fear
was the first time I saw that man
standing with his spear.
His armour shone bright in the sun
I knew this wasn't to be fun.
Then he cried 'You're sure to die
from my many powers.'

That was it I gave the order then
I ran across the border.
Arrows flew into his crew and they
fell like burning towers.
Throughout the battle they turned insane,
but we kept fighting strong, in vain.
Many men were felled they say
on that day in sunny May.

Andrew Barratclough (11)
Red House School

LITTLE TOMMY

Tommy was a funny boy,
He never bothered with a toy,
He sucked all day on his dummy,
Nothing else soothed his tummy.
Until one day it all went wrong,
He sucked his dummy far too long,
Little Tommy started coughing.
At first his father just said nothing,
But the dummy had been swallowed whole,
And Tommy's eyes began to roll.
Poor, old Tommy's face was shocking,
His intestines started knotting.
Tommy began to gasp and wheeze,
'Spit out that dummy,' said Dad, 'Oh please.'
He spluttered and took his last breath,
Tommy had sucked himself to death.

Joe Starkie (11)
Red House School

CAT

Remember
The way you can stroke
Its soft silken coat;
The warm weight
Of its body
As it lies with closed eyes
On your lap.

Forget
The razor-sharp claws
That spring from its paws,
The hiss from the bush,
The glowing eyes in the dark
That stare at you endlessly.

Christopher Cook (13)
Red House School

LIZARD

Think of its long pink tongue
Flickering quickly from its mouth
Like a blow out at a party;
Of each shining scale
On its flexing tail,
As it plays in the sun,
Has fun.

Forget its small quickly-moving eyes
Which dart from side to side,
And its diet of flies.

Swaguna Mahapatra (13)
Red House School

JELLYFISH

Smile
At its see-through body
Glittering as it hangs
Like a parachute in the rippling water;
At the rainbow threads
Floating from side to side
On the tide,
Swaying without direction
For eternity.

Shudder
At its ancient tentacles
Which sting like a swarm of vicious bees;
At poison in a dancing fairy shape.

Kelly Harris (13)
Red House School

POLAR BEAR

Beware,
The snow-white polar bear can glide
Through the snow and hide,
His flexible shape can bend
And blend in with the snow.
His paws have claws
Which can shred a seal or penguin
And leave him dead in seconds.
He will not give you a bear hug!
Run for your life,
From that gorgeous teddy bear
Standing there
In the snow.

Simon Avery (13)
Red House School

EAGLE

Celebrate its swoop, its glide,
It's shining in the sun.
Its golden beak, its eyes of fire
As it flies by.

Celebrate its calm landing,
Its clenching claws on rock,
The lifting of its warm brown wings
As it dives down
Down to the distant ground.

Regret the look of hate in its eye
The smell of death
On its breath
That makes my head spin.

Jonathan Amerigo (13)
Red House School

WHITE TIGER

Display his exquisite body,
His soft,white coat
As bright as glittering snow
When the dazzling sun shines
Rippling over his smooth muscles,
Display his lean length
His curling twitching tail.

Push away his ear shattering roar,
His sharpened knife-like paw
Which clearly say,
'I am here and I am king,
Today and always.'

Aileigh Brough (13)
Red House School

BLACK WIDOW SPIDER

Remember
The eight little legs
Like loops of thread,
The startling pattern
On its back and head,
The sly way it walks
And stalks its prey,
Several times each day.

Forget the venomous sting,
The way it can spring
From under the toilet seat,
The way it shines in the light
At night.

Greg Cuthbert (13)
Red House School

THE BEE

Remember
Its small spherical shape in the air,
The way pollen sticks to its furry back
Like blobs of yellow candle wax,
The way its delicate wings whirr
Invisibly and soundlessly.
Remember the dripping honeycomb.

Forget
Its zooming flight in your direction,
The way it dies to sting,
The sting wrenched out of its body,
Left in your flesh,
Fatal to some.

Alice Jones (14)
Red House School

WINTER

Cold winds whistling through the bare trees,
Snow falling softly and children on their knees.
Snowballs, snowmen, sledging down the hill,
Warm mince pies and Christmas cake, be sure to eat your fill.

The blackness and the darkness,
The rain and the snow,
Hats and gloves and icicles,
How the wind does blow.

Long shopping trips, coloured lights,
Loads of parties too.
This is my favourite season . . .

       Winter.

Katie Sheen (11)
Red House School

THE JOURNEY

The bright, yellow moon was shining on the black sea,
Revealing its gentle, undulating motion.
A fishing boat was beginning what would be
A long, dangerous journey to a distant ocean.

To fish in the Arctic was its aim,
At a time when all was night.
Then having filled the boat, to return again,
Having fished for all its might.

The bright, yellow moon, was shining on the black sea
When the boat returned once more.
Safe home to the harbour's lee,
Home to its own safe shore.

Steven Gordon (11)
Red House School

CLIPPED WINGS

They laugh,
They stare, they punch and kick,
At my expense they think I'm thick,
A tear runs down my bruised and beaten face,
I see school as a dark and dingy place,
Where bullies hide and leap out at you,
They tell you things you never knew,
'You're too fat,'
'You're too thin,'
'Your face doesn't fit go back to your rubbish bin,'
I'm sure they wouldn't like it if we said it back to them,
But no, we hide away,
Day after day,
They are the hawk and we are the prey.

Helen Roberts (11)
Red House School

BEAR

Take care,
The bear can sink his huge teeth
Into a slippery fish
As it flashes by in the freezing stream
He can slash with his claw
And rip it apart,
Stop its heart with one blow.
His deep brown coat looks warm,
But his heart is cold.
He could do the same to you.

Richard Plenderleith (14)
Red House School

A FAT HOG DOWN A MANHOLE

The day was so bright
that the terrorism in America was reversed,
wars stopped around the world,
and Middlesbrough finally reached the finals
and won the FA Cup.

In Kensington a fat hog fell down a manhole and squealed.

Skateboarders skated well away from the park,
because concentration is difficult when a hog squeals,
and a plump farmer argued with a security guard:
'That hog's been there since morning;
you should do something.'

Towards evening the moon stared down, shining immensely,
and clouds passed overhead in a curious fashion,
but still the hog squealed.

Then along came two boys and climbed down the hole.
A hobo put down his blanket and clambered down after.

Their way led across the savage sewage pits.
The expedition was like a trip into deep moon craters;
like Theseus's gauntlet-run in the Labyrinth.
The hog fell silent; the boys and the hobo became rocks;
the wind stopped howling; and the sewage water moved aside;
the Earth stood still;
time stopped.
The hobo extended his arm.

It was like a the landing of Apollo 13 on Earth;
it caught the hog.

They returned up the ladder
to the solo
of the fat hog's grunting.

Aaron Ray (12)
Red House School

PARTY!

My friends are telling me,
About a party up in NYC,
Will I make it?
Down right,
I'll be on the next flight.

In the car
At the bar,
This is so much fun!
It's going by so quickly,
My stomach feels tickly.

Then I see him . . .

The boy of my dreams,
The one who's head of all the teams,
Is right in front of me,
And with a flick of the hair,
He's right there.

I'm waiting for the question,
There's so much tension,
Here it comes,
'Will you dance with me?'
My heart is in my knee!

'Yes, of course, I'd love to!'
It is the best do, I've ever been to,
I'll come here again, but only with Danny,
He is the best,
Better than the rest!

Lauren Summers (11)
Red House School

LIFE AND DEATH

You're born, like an angel from heaven.
Your face is a portrait of beauty.
Your eyes, a blinding blue,
Your cheeks, a rosy red.

As you grow older your beauty grows,
Your features become more defined.
Your lips, the colour of blood
Your hair a golden cloak.

You're no longer a child - now an adult
You have your own life.
Your future lays before you like a patchwork of opportunities.
You're an independent woman.

You now have your own children
You're at your prime of life.
You have a successful job
Your beauty shines like a blazing fire.

You're getting old - but your beauty's not fading;
Your inner child showing through.
You're now retired, but life's not over,
You're watching your children grow.

You're so old now you're ready to go.
You've lived your life.
You've had your adventures,
You float to heaven - the same angel that came down.

Charlotte Kitchen (13)
Red House School

SCRAPS

I'm here to warn you scraps are bad,
For tummy, health and even Dad.
Never eat scraps they'll do you harm,
Not even with their dirty charm.
There was one girl who made this mistake,
Contemplating a nasty fate,
Who would have dreamt little Sally Clarke,
Would eat from bins in the local park?
She sat and ate for hours and hours,
Even the foxes' mouths turned sour.
You don't see it every day,
A cute, little girl of early May,
Chewing upon a half-eaten burger,
Oh it gets worse, I can't go much further.
The sandwich you threw away,
Well what can I say?
In her mouth or further south,
You wanting it now, I very much doubt,
But very shortly she took to her bed,
Because little Sally Clarke was very much dead.
So take my advice scraps are bad,
Unless you want to end up very sad,
Or have your story told to strangers,
Not yet aware of the many dangers.
So don't bother trying,
Or you'll end up dying,
While I just keep sighing and sighing.

Sophie Pott (11)
Red House School

AUTUMN

How I love these days of September,
Those long, misty mornings,
The sky turning grey,
The weatherman's warning.

The nights become longer,
As the days grow much shorter,
The autumn leaves fall,
And ice forms on water.

Children hunt for conkers,
On horse chestnut trees,
Hats, scarves and warm gloves,
As fingers start to freeze.

The clocks go back in October,
Mornings and evenings are dark,
No playing after school's out,
No late games in the park,

At Hallowe'en witches go on the prowl,
Ghosts dress up in white sheets,
Knocking loudly at neighbours' doors,
Children playing 'Trick or Treat?'

November the 5th is drawing near,
Guy Fawkes is sitting on the bonfire,
Sparklers, rockets and Catherine wheels,
The flames leap higher and higher.

Emily-Jane Saxby (11)
Red House School

I Knew a Girl Called Molly

I knew a girl called Molly,
And she was bright and jolly.
But all day long her infatuation
Was sitting in front of her PlayStation.

Evening, afternoon and morning,
She wouldn't listen to the warning.
'It's bad for you,' her mother cried.
'I'm having a rest,' young Molly lied.

But then upon a Tuesday morning,
Just about as day was dawning.
Molly got up and one hour later,
Her eyes were square, like paper!

Oh the noise young Molly made,
Her mother just said you shouldn't have laid,
Flat out like the top of a table,
Drawing electricity from out of our cable.

Then all her life poor Molly was blind,
So get this inside your rightful mind,
Don't stay inside all night and day,
Playing all your life away.

For if you do you might, just might,
Be parted with your precious sight!

William Naylor (11)
Red House School

TIGER

Smile at his tail
Which flickers in surprise,
At the gleaming gold of his eyes,
At the muscles which ripple
Under his smartly-striped coat
As he speeds beneath trees,
At his teeth which shine
Bright in the light.

Flinch at the paws
Holding razor claws,
At his rumbling growl
Tumbling towards you,
At eyes seeking you out,
At teeth ready to rip.

Ronnie Love (13)
Red House School

STUDENT

There is a student who is very prudent,
He spends all day playing with hay,
And eating fishfingers on Friday.
He didn't really linger when sticking his finger up his nose,
Then striking a pose and wiggling his toes.
Then shouting ye foes, nobody knows how to wiggle their toes.

Nathan Young (12)
Red House School

'BORO

Gooooaaaallll!
Two - one to us, two - one, that is right.
The ball came in, a cross from the left
What a sight.
Ehiogu's header, the crowd went wild
The header was strong it was not mild.
Mclaren's change, who's coming on?
Oh look it's Paul Okon,
Off goes Mustoe, disappointed
An early bath to get anointed.
There's the third, Greening's strike
He's said to Newcastle 'On yer bike!'
There's the whistle
Paul Durkin blows
Off goes Boksic, there he goes.
I leave this rhyme to make a stand
Mclaren's a man in demand.

Matt Lockwood (12)
St Patrick's RC Comprehensive School

THE RAINBOW

Red is like a rose blossoming in the rain,
Yellow is the colour of the big, bright sun,
Green is the grass sparkling from the dew,
Orange is like the blazing fire lighting up the dark, night sky,
Violet is a plant that grows in the summer,
Indigo and blue are like the dark night sky,
People say there's a pot of gold at the end of a rainbow.

Clare Thompson (12)
St Patrick's RC Comprehensive School

LIFE AND TIME

It is the winter of '66
While man walks upon land.
Time changes as I live
While snow falls upon me.

I'm thinking about thinking
Love, hatred, aggression
What does it mean?
What can I do?

Curiosity, wonder
What is wonder?
Belief, law,
Why be called the law?

I am curious
I want to know
Who am I?
Why be called what I'm called?

This is my poem
What is a poem?
I don't know!
But I want to learn.

Matthew McGee (11)
St Patrick's RC Comprehensive School

FOOTY

Footy is fantastic,
Your shin pads are made of plastic,
Your shorts have elastic,
That's footy, fantastic.

Gareth Cox (14)
St Patrick's RC Comprehensive School

THE ICE FIGURE

Freezing cold night
My hands are red and numb
I feel like needles are striking my face
And yet this man does not offer his gloves
Nor his hat and scarf
His eyes staring coldly
His grin sends shivers down my spine
His arms like twigs, look about to snap
He's as wide as an old oak tree
And as tall as me.

Suddenly the moon shines upon him
His grin becomes friendly, now I can see
His eyes feeling as they sparkle in the moonlight
Unblinking he's staring at me,
But I'm not scared
He's my friend
I creep up to bed
He gazes from outside,
But the next morning he's just a pool of water.

Rhiannon Beckett (12)
St Patrick's RC Comprehensive School

WHAT IF?

What if space was where we lived?
What if computers didn't exist?
What if music couldn't be heard?
What if colours couldn't be seen?
What if everything was like one thing?
Then would we still be the same?

Andrew Farndale (15)
St Patrick's RC Comprehensive School

MY DAY

Today I'm going kayaking
I'll try some bell boats too
I'll be looking out for fishermen
Along the river so blue.
But first I've got my lessons
So many of them to get through
It seems a really long time
A huge map here, a poem there
Pieces of work coming from everywhere
A game of football
That wasn't so bad
A bit of a kick around with all the lads.
At last the time came and the last bell rang
The doors slammed back with a great, big bang.
I zoomed out the doorway and down all the steps
Onto the minibus I really leaped.
We went down the road and round the corner
Over the bridge and through the gates
I got into my gear, the same as my mates
We launch our kayaks and row downstream.

Philip Smith (12)
St Patrick's RC Comprehensive School

SKATE PARK

I go to the skate park on Tuesdays
Skateboards, BMX, blades and scooters too
Go up the ramps and into the pit
Spinning, wheelies and grinds.
Baggy trousers, baggy tops, pads on knees
And helmet on top.

Spills and thrills
I get hot and dirty, I fall and get bruised
I've made lots of friends, some old, some new
It's fun, it's great.
I always get into trouble when I come home late.

David Golden (11)
St Patrick's RC Comprehensive School

FOOT-AND-MOUTH

They call it FMD, but what does it mean?
The news does not mention it now
So is it over?
The answer is no and far from it.
Farms and land are still desolate
The invisible disease casts shadows over lives
Farmers are broken and desperate
A wave of smoke fills the infected areas
Dead and grotesque, the helpless animals lie waiting,
Waiting to be burned.
They say it thrives in wet and cold weather
So will it be back by winter?
Who knows?
The gallons and gallons of disinfectant used
At least someone may have made a profit
For the rest, however it is different isn't it?
If you're not affected it is not important
Until there is nothing left
For farmers it is a time of worry and concern
Waiting to see if their lives will hit rock-bottom
Will they see themselves lose everything
Or will they have a lucky escape?

Faye McDearmid (14)
St Patrick's RC Comprehensive School

NINE JOYFUL CHILDREN

Nine joyful children
One forgot his bait
He went home to get it
Then there were eight.

Eight joyful children
One was nearly eleven
He went in to get his lunch
Then there were seven.

Seven naughty children
Were playing with some sticks
One was chased by a dog
Then there were six.

Six joyful children
Were looking at a beehive
A bee chased a boy
And then there were five.

Five joyful children
Were at the headmaster's door
The headmaster told one to get away
Then there were four.

Four joyful children
One hurt his knee
He ran off crying
Then there were three.

Three joyful children
One caught the flu
He went to tell the teacher
Then there were two.

Two joyful children
Saw the one that had gone
One of them chased him
Then there was one.

One naughty child
Was walking alone
He went to find some friends
Then there were none.

Damon Towes (14)
St Patrick's RC Comprehensive School

THE SEA

It twinkles like a star
As I walk across the shore
The sunset goes down
There is no light, anymore.

The stars light up the sky
So I can see the perfect ray
Of the light that comes my way.
The waves are very silent
As I stroll along the shore.

The whole beach is asleep
Until morning comes
The sun pops up as
The blossom blooms.

The dolphins and the whales
Come to the horizon
As the sea is awaking
And early morning is rising!

Leah Iveson (13)
St Patrick's RC Comprehensive School

MY LOST FRIEND

He steps in a light, the glimmering sun
Then he falls like the proud lion loosing his prey
Still not moving, the corpse lying there
A dark veil over him like the night sky
Round his neck, soaking the life out of him.
Still he lies there.

A young girl crying like never before
She weeps over the young man.
Still he lies there.

Then he is put into the ditch, dark and gloomy
Slam! Slam! Mud being thrown on top
Heat coming up like being in an oven.
Still he lies there.

Suddenly a glimmering light came through the clouds
On to the graves and then it was gone
Like a light being turned on and off.
Is he still there now?

James Adams (12)
St Patrick's RC Comprehensive School

DREAMS

Last night while I lay sleeping
Upon my feather bed
I drifted into a whirlpool
Of dreams inside my head.

Was I really dreaming
Or is this my own world?
I couldn't think right now
As my mind twirled and twirled.

I was thrown out of darkness
And into reality
I'll never know what my dreams
Are about until they grab back hold of me.

Hayley Jobson (12)
St Patrick's RC Comprehensive School

GOING FISHING

The alarm clock sounds at 3am,
My mate Andy is full of joy.
We set off on our trip to find the hungry cod
We arrive at 5am and ragworms here we come.
We dig and dig and dig until we find the worms
They can't escape my quick hands
Now they're on the hook.
I cast out with the power of an ox
Now the bait is gone.
I strike and it's a big one,
The cod surrenders to the man
He dips his head in shame,
This is the end of his life.
He's going on the plate
Now it's all gone quiet
Time to give the spinner a go
I cast into the breaking waves
The fish are coming now
It's getting cold now
I think it's time to go.
I'll take my catch home
I'm going to have a feast,
Until next time Scarborough
Until next we meet.

Jamie Robson (12)
St Patrick's RC Comprehensive School

FEAR

You're walking home
It's late at night
The sky is black
Like a blind man's sight.

You quicken your pace
Your breath rate increases
Sickening images dart through your head
You mind explodes into pieces.

You can already see the headlines
You never know what might happen
So tragic at first,
But after a week all is forgotten.

The adrenaline gushes through your veins
Like a speeding car on a highway
You just want to get home, is it so much to ask?
You wish you could retreat safely away.

You're in a half jog, half run state now
Can feel the blood speed past your ears
The hair on the back of the neck starts to grow
Is that shadow drawing nearer?

Panic-stricken, you begin to tremble
Possibilities racing through your mind
How did you get yourself into this?
Why the hell set off at this time?

One more block to go
Barely breathing you begin to sprint
You see your door so you sprint some more
Not daring to stop and think.

The door slams shut safely behind you
You breath a sigh of relief
You feel a bit silly now for being so scared
You'll never put yourself through it again in your life.

But we all know temptation makes you stay longer
You don't think of the consequences until the time
When you're facing fear, yet again
And again you'll relive this rhyme!

Michelle Carter (15)
St Patrick's RC Comprehensive School

THE SEA

It twinkles like a ruby
As I walk across the shore
The sunset goes down
There is no light any more.

The stars light up the sky
So I can see the perfect ray
Of light that comes my way.
The waves are very silent
And the sand is too.

The whole beach is asleep
Until morning comes.
The sun pops up and blossoms
Bloom.

The dolphins and whales
And fishes too can smell
The ice cream, bread and candy
In the sea air.

Claire Sturdy (13)
St Patrick's RC Comprehensive School

MY NANA KATH

Nana Kath, I said bye
Oh Nana Kath, why did you die?
The family misses you
You were my nana,
We really love you,
I miss you.

The funeral came,
Glad she didn't go in the flames,
Nana you were the best
Have a good rest.
Every week we go to your grave
Me and my mam pray.

I love you Nana Kath.

Matthew Hall (13)
St Patrick's RC Comprehensive School

THE DOLPHIN

I sit on the sandy beach
Staring, staring
Just gazing into space
I then cast my eyes out to sea
Then suddenly I see
The most beautiful thing that's oh so special to me
A graceful, dazeful dolphin
Jumping playfully in and out the waves
The dolphin does not laze
I just sit and gaze.

Rebecca Newbold (11)
St Patrick's RC Comprehensive School

FIRE

Fire, orange, yellow, red and hot
Cavemen they used it for the cooking pot,
But now and these days it gets out of hand
Many people die with the flick of its wrist.
Spreads real quick with real mighty twist
No one and nothing can stop this blaze
Destroying and trashing in a real winding maze.
Later on when everything is black
The fire dies down, it's receiving no more oxygen back
After hour, after hour the firemen come
There's no more fire, everything gone.
Kids and people beware, fire is not a game
And one more thing . . . it can't be *tamed!*

Samantha Remmer (12)
St Patrick's RC Comprehensive School

A TREACHEROUS NIGHT

The night draws in, it's started to rain
The raindrops hit hard on my windowpane.
The howling gale surrounds my home
I'm cosy inside as I write this poem.
I'm glad I'm inside on this treacherous night
I look outside and see all the lights
Of the passing cars and the people outside
Wanting to be home by their fireside.
I hope the morning brings a better day
As I get up and ready to make my way
To school . . .

Rob Illingworth (12)
St Patrick's RC Comprehensive School

THE LEAVES IN THE TREE

The leaves they fall down from the tree
    Let them shower down on me.
All the colours, dark 'n' bright
    They fall throughout the day and night.

They form a carpet on the floor
    Nice and soft for where I walk.

The poor trees, they look so bare
    It's a pity they don't have hair.
Are they warm? Are they cold?
    They are brave, they are bold.

They have no leaves through the cold season
    I wonder what is the reason
This is the time they need them most
    To keep them lovely and warm as toast.

Michael Wass (12)
St Patrick's RC Comprehensive School

THE RAINBOW

Do you see the rainbow in the grey sky?
Floating through the air in the sky above.
What keeps it there I wonder, does it fly?
Like the blackbird, sparrow and the dove.
Red like the scarlet colour of the rose
Sherwood green Robin Hood's favourite clothes.
Indigo-blue almost black as the night
Orangy-yellow, a canary in flight.
Forget-me-nots and violets cover the ground,
Raindrops falling: what a wonderful sound.

Rebecca Latham (12)
St Patrick's RC Comprehensive School

IF . . .

If I had one million friends,
I'd dine with them till night end.
If I had a submarine,
I'd search the ocean floors so green.
If I had a guardian angel,
I'd rock it in a golden cradle.
If I had a time machine,
I'd go back to see the long-lost queens.
If I had a load of money,
I'd spend it all on loads of honey.
If I had a teddy bear,
I'd make sure it had all my care.
If I had a bed so comfy,
I'd definitely say I'm really lucky.
If I had a sea of my own,
I'd catch a wave I would have flown.
If . . .

Jennifer Leighton (12)
St Patrick's RC Comprehensive School

SEASONS

S ummer is hot
E aster, chocolate eggs
A utumn is when the leaves fall
S pring is for little lambs
O pening presents on Christmas Day
N ew toys at Christmas
S anta comes down the chimney.

Stacey Gavaghan (13)
St Patrick's RC Comprehensive School

SEASONS

The wind is blowing,
The snow is snowing,
The trees are blossoming,
The seasons are showing.

The sun is blazing,
The flowers are growing,
The sun lotion is selling,
The seasons are showing.

The spring is producing,
The trees are blossoming,
The flowers are growing,
The seasons are showing.

The snow is snowing,
The cold is bitter,
The frost is chilly,
The seasons are showing.

The sky is dull,
The leaves are browning,
The leaves are falling,
The seasons are showing.

The wind is blowing,
The snow is snowing,
The trees are blossoming,
The seasons are showing.

Jamie Green (12)
St Patrick's RC Comprehensive School

THE FERRY BEAST

As we entered the Beast
This great, metal Behemoth
We heard it surge into life
Deeper, deeper we were dragged
Into the Beast's belly
Past skeletons of long dead lorries.

This cavernous stomach
It towered above us
Lots more cars trapped!

As I stood I heard the heart
Pulsating down below
We clambered up
To stare at the water
From the top of the Behemoth Ferry.

With an ear-splitting roar it began to move
Fish scattered, water splashed
It thrashed its way out to sea
On a journey without a seen end.

Crash! Clang! Clatter! Crunch!
We're free, it's breached
The great doors lie open.

The ramps comes down like a silver tongue
We drove away
Escaped just as it left
Back away to sea.

Philip Turnham (13)
St Patrick's RC Comprehensive School

GOING FISHING

The alarm bell sounds at 3am.
Me and Jamie are full of excitement
We're going on a fishing trip, we're going to catch a big one
We arrive at 4:45am and ragworm here we come.
On the sand we go, we dig deeper and deeper
Until we get our deadly bait.
I cast out with the power of a buffalo
My bait is gone, oh, oh it's goin' to be a big one
The massive cod surrenders.
It will be in my tummy in a couple of hours.
I cast a spinner, here come the fish
The fish are jumping on my line, I can't get enough of them
Well our trip's been a good one
It will be better next time.

Andrew Hardy (12)
St Patrick's RC Comprehensive School

RUNNING WATER

Water, crystal clear, a pool of light
   Flowing endlessly among the edges
Starting to rush in a rapid motion
   Colliding with rocks, wearing away banks,
Crushing everything in its winding path
   Surging round bends of debris, splashing,
Consuming whatever it wants to have
   Gushing round in oceans, seas and rivers
The babbling brook, the lazy river
   The cool spray of rain, the sweetness of dew.

James Henderson (12)
St Patrick's RC Comprehensive School

WHY DO WE GO TO SCHOOL?

Why do we need to go to school?
To have a laugh, to play the fool?
Why do we need to slave away
At a desk, day after day?
Or is it to help us get on in life
To get a job, to help us strive?
To meet our friends, make new ones too
Who cheer us up when we are blue.
Though I sometimes wonder about the staff,
Who you hardly see having a laugh
Or playing the fool or having fun,
Although you do always get some
Who really aren't ever glum.
They're the ones that like to teach
And hardly, hardly ever preach.
Just make you laugh and enjoy learning
To secure in the future, you'll make a good earning.

Lauren Barclay (13)
St Patrick's RC Comprehensive School

A STRAY

Not knowing when his next meal is
He creeps beside the bin
Looking for bits of scrap.
Suddenly he finds a tuna tin
Covered in soggy bread
In this tin is a little morsel
Of tuna and scrap.
Quickly he gollops it down
Not knowing when he'll get another
Meal!

Racheal Moy (11)
St Patrick's RC Comprehensive School

I Lie Awake

I lie awake unable to sleep
For weeks I haven't slept a peep
I sit and cry the night away
All I want to do is get up and play.

People do not understand
They don't know what's on my mind
They all say that I'm so sweet,
But when they do I burn with heat.

If I don't tell someone soon
I will burst like a balloon
I hold my head and stand tall,
But inside I want to fall.

Leah Kelly (12)
St Patrick's RC Comprehensive School

Sharks

The colossal carnivores of the sea
With silver, metallic skin, silky, smooth
Stealthily gliding through the blue ocean like torpedoes
Deep, jet-black eyes like bottomless pits
It floats effortlessly through the deep, blue sea.

When it's hungry
Its eyes roll over white
Its teeth glimmering like diamonds
It goes for the attack
Hated by the world for its will to survive
To eat the flesh of anything it can find
This is just another part of nature in the deep, blue sea.

Adam Porteous (13)
St Patrick's RC Comprehensive School

ANGELS

Does everyone have a guardian angel
Is it just a lie?
If it's true, then why don't they
Protect you from the Devil's eye?

Do they float around the sky
On a cloud, fluffy and light?
Do they have a halo
That shines a radiant light?

Are they invisible to us
And not within our sight?
Are they just the burning stars
That we observe at night?

Amanda White (12)
St Patrick's RC Comprehensive School

TIME TO GO

You went away,
But we wanted you to stay
I guess it was your time to go.
You left us feeling sad
And we were all so mad
That it was your time to go.
We know where you are
And it seems so far,
All 'cos it was your time to go.
We know we'll see you soon
Far beyond the moon,
When it's our time to go.

Lyndsey Walker (14)
St Patrick's RC Comprehensive School

FOOTBALL

The whistle blows
Three o'clock in the afternoon
I'm on the bench
I hope I'm playing soon.

I'm freezing cold
No goals have been scored
And I'm still on the board.

Just a minute
The pace is getting faster
The opposition scores a goal
Oh, what a disaster.

Stuart Blackburn (13)
St Patrick's RC Comprehensive School

FIREWORKS

The glittering lights explode in the sky
The rockets fly up and up high
Little children with sparklers in their hands
Like a wicked witch with her magic wand.
The silent pause between each firework
As it screeches up and away, then stops with a jerk
Noses red with a bitter cold
Everyone watching, the young and the old
The amazement of the colours so bright
Red, blue, green and white.
Babies cry with the sounds so loud
After exploding all that's left is a smoky cloud.

Stephanie Burns (13)
St Patrick's RC Comprehensive School

WATCHES

Their shiny countenance flickers and glitters in the light
Its longish, pointy hands orbit thousands of times, even at night
Their contents stay concealed behind a small, steel case
In which are nuts and cogs that rotate sluggishly behind its shell
Like a snail slithering, slimily along wet, cool blades of grass.

It ticks like a bomb
Ready to explode
It sits elegantly on our wrists
Keeping our time safe and impregnable
Within its all important, longish, pointy, narrow hands.

Their hands orbit its face, like Earth
Which orbits the huge ball of essential fire which floats in space,
But as time goes by
It slowly begins to die
And, on one of those days it shall stop its ticks and tocks.

Jay Kelly (12)
St Patrick's RC Comprehensive School

I CAN'T, I CAN

I can draw like an artist as my pencil draws a picture,
But I can't sculpture like an artist as a hand drops off my model.

I can cry like a baby as a tear drops on my pillow,
But I can't sing like a bird when it sings on the rooftops.

I can swim like a fish as it glides through the water,
But I can't run like the wind as it gusts at eighty miles per hour.

But who cares what I can do?
I do.

Rebecca Oliver (15)
St Patrick's RC Comprehensive School

GOD BLESS AMERICA

God bless America, Tuesday 11th September
As tragedy struck New York's World Trade Center
Two hijacked aircraft hit the famous Twin Towers
Beyond the control of everyone's powers.

Nothing could be done but to watch in disbelief
As the world shared in New York City's grief
Local police officers and firemen arrive without delay
Not knowing what they faced in the display.

Never in history have we witnessed such a crime
And altered forever the New York skyline
Dust like snow filled the air all around
Whilst these two buildings were smashed to the ground.

Our hearts have been saddened by the lives that were lost
Your faces have shown us this tragedy has cost
As you stand with your pain in deepest sorrow
We are with you today, we'll be with you tomorrow.

Jenna Sharp (15)
St Patrick's RC Comprehensive School

MY SPECIAL GRANDAD

I lie awake and think
What happened to the man,
The kind and loving man that once stood there
Holding my tiny hand.
Each day I was with him I felt so special
So close to his side I knew I was his petal.
You took him away and now he is gone
Why, why? But what's gone is gone
To a better place.

Katie Fairbairn (12)
St Patrick's RC Comprehensive School

LIFE

Do you ever think of the future?
Do you ever think of the past?
Do you ever think of the present?
How long you will last?

Your life is like a clock
Just ticking away
For every minute
For every day.

Will it ever stop
Or will it last forever?
Will you expect it
Or maybe never?

Strike you down like lightning
You fall on the spot
You're colder than ice
And you're stiff as a rock
This is the end of the clock.

Danny Wood (15)
St Patrick's RC Comprehensive School

MY BROTHER'S DOG

My brother has a little dog
Who is called Ice
He likes dog biscuits
He thinks they're very nice.
If you feed him lots and lots
He'll end up being sick
He won't even budge if you poke him
With a stick!

Michael Cartwright (11)
St Patrick's RC Comprehensive School

A Day In The Life Of A Footballer

I woke up knowing full well
It was my big day
I was so nervous
My belly was rumbling like an earthquake.

I was on my way to the ground
To play the best football I can.

I stood in the tunnel
I can hear the crowd
Walking out I could hear them
Like a roar of tongues.

Playing the match I hear
The crowd chanting my name
I knew this was my one
And only dream.

Lee Robinson (15)
St Patrick's RC Comprehensive School

What?

What happens when you die?
Do you still exist?
Do you live on?
Do you see God?
Do you become an animal?
Do heaven and hell exist?
Does God exist?
Does everyone die?
Where will I go when I die?

Caitlin Harrison (11)
St Patrick's RC Comprehensive School

TWIN TOWERS

The sun rose like the Lord flicked a switch to dawn a new day
It started like a normal day,
No one was to know what was to come
They swarmed into work like bees to a hive,
It was a normal day until the first plane came,
The people in the towers were shocked and petrified,
But yet did they know another plane was to collide
When it was over it was a sad sight
Those two great, tall buildings in ruins on the floor,
For the people who gave up their lives,
For their children and wives a great deal of respect is given to them,
The way they went to save people's lives
From the bowels of hell.

Lee Jones (15)
St Patrick's RC Comprehensive School

THINKING ABOUT TOMORROW

I like to go and rest in bed
A place to rest my aching head
I like to think about tomorrow
And the things I may not have done.

Just to think people may die in sorrow
Or that people may be born
As I look out the window night-time turns to dawn.
I like to think about tomorrow
It's weird, I just do
I wonder what friends I'll meet
Or which friends I may lose . . .

Stephen Powls (12)
St Patrick's RC Comprehensive School

ANGER

They won't watch or listen - they don't even care
They say that you're 'at that age'
Though you try to ignore it, the fury's still there,
Like a tiger, prowling locked up in a cage.

Whirling, swirling, clouding your mind
Confusion, frustration and fear
All reason, all logic is left far behind
As anger engulfs every thought and idea.

Then suddenly it bursts into flame -
Ignited by the tiniest spark
Lashing down on them all, like boiling hot rain,
Angry lightning erupts in the peaceful dark.

Words are screamed, feelings torn
The fire spreads everywhere
Emotions whipped up in this terrible storm
Are thrown at the people who once did not care.

Fists are clenched, eyes are burning
Scorching tears flow free
Spirits are crushed but at least they are learning,
Not to ignore the rage inside me.

Eleanor Gaynor (14)
St Patrick's RC Comprehensive School

WWF HEROES

Mick Foley, Mick Foley the god,
Once Mankind then Cactus Jack
He lost his chance
In a Hell in the Cell match,
Became commissioner for a year or two,
He never came back now he is back
He is the new commissioner.

Matt, Jeff and Lita,
They make Team Extreme
With a Swanton Bomb
And a Twist of Fate
On Booker-T and Test,
They are the new WCW Tag Team champs,
They fought many times they're no 1,
They are the Tag Team Champs.

Alex Dorrington (11)
St Patrick's RC Comprehensive School

ON THE 11TH SEPTEMBER

On the 11th September
The New York skyline
Changed forever.
The Twin Towers
That once stood proud
Were hit by two planes
And they crashed to the ground.
People were shocked,
People were scared,
Firefighters went back
Because no one else dared.
To search for people that lay buried there
Some were silent, some just cried,
As the graves were dug
For the people who had died
One thing that no one will forget is
On the 11th September
The New York skyline
Changed forever.

Clare Peacock (14)
St Patrick's RC Comprehensive School

A DAY NEVER TO BE FORGOTTEN

Silence swept across the nation like a blanket of snow,
Eyes glued to televisions worldwide,
Shocked faces watched in disbelief,
Confused people tried to understand,
Whilst the destruction sets in.

Grief shadowed our nation like a dark, gloomy cloud,
United in sadness,
As they viewed the horrific scenes,
Twin Towers crumbled to the ground like a pack of playing cards,
This day never to be forgotten,
Is of course September 11th.

R.I.P.

Kayleigh Hope (15)
St Patrick's RC Comprehensive School

FATHER CHRISTMAS

I think the Christmas spirit is quite dead
Because of an obese man in red.
Delivering presents to girls and boys
Brain washing them with shiny toys.
That evil man on a flying sleigh
Bringing so much misery on Christmas Day.
He breaks into your house,
He doesn't bother to ask
Only to carry out his sickening task.
This man of course is Santa Claus,
The evil man who breaks all the laws.
And we all know when he'll strike next
Leaving everyone quite perplexed!

Shaun Smith (14)
St Patrick's RC Comprehensive School

LIFE!

Why are we alive?
What's going to happen to us?
What are we going to do tomorrow?
Do you know? I don't.

Was life for children?
Was life for jobs?
Was life for helping?
Or was life for mobs?

The clock is ticking,
Years go by,
What is life for?
Are we all going to die?

What is life for?
Do you know? I don't.

Amy Green (11)
St Patrick's RC Comprehensive School

I LIKE . . .

I like purple,
but don't like blue
I like ice cream,
but don't like stew

I like red,
but don't like mustard
I like biscuits,
but don't like custard

Any way who cares what I like?
- I do.

Laura Payne (14)
St Patrick's RC Comprehensive School

DREAM OR NOT?

Night is dark
I see a spark
My dog will bark
I watch a film about a shark.

I see a bat going to a nest
The birds are singing they're a pest
It's getting creepy
I'm so sleepy.

I hear clicking
It's getting louder
I see a puff of powder
My nana came out and said
'Howdy.'

Katie Poppleton (12)
St Patrick's RC Comprehensive School

MY DAD

I don't see my dad early in the morning,
I don't see my dad awake,
But I know he is better
And I don't see him in pain,
Nor suffering again.
I know he is in a better place
Although I don't see him.
I know he is still free
And at peace again.
I know I will see him one day
In heaven, in paradise.

Hellen Frost (13)
St Patrick's RC Comprehensive School

SPORTS

Sports

S is for sport
P is for professionals
O is for Olympics, the main sport
R is for Rivaldo, the best in the world
T is for tennis, the best sport in the world
S is for sport, something for all.

Owen

O wen
W inning again
E ngland's hero
N ever lets us down.

Daniel Flynn (12)
St Patrick's RC Comprehensive School

FIREWORKS

F lying high through the sky
I n the darkness of the night
R otating, speeding faster and faster
E cstatic the children shout and whoop
W onderful colours explode into more
O verpowering sounds, we scream for more
R ockets, Catherine wheels, fireworks galore
K indly entertaining us in their plight
S parkling beautiful in the twilight.

Matthew Brown (11)
St Patrick's RC Comprehensive School

CHRISTMAS

Snowflakes falling on the ground
Fairy lights all around
A warm fire lights up the room
Santa will be here soon
Bringing sweets, bikes and toys
For every single girl and boy.

I lay awake trying to sleep
Then I hear something creak
As I look into the cold, black air
I see Santa with snow-white hair
Suddenly I feel tired and weak
Before I know it I'm in the land of sleep.

I wake up in my nice, warm bed
Then excitement fills my head
Christmas morning is so great
I ran downstairs, I couldn't wait
Christmas presents surround the tree
All these presents just for me
Clothes, sweets even sticky glue
I hope you have a good Christmas too.

Leanne Trotter (11)
St Patrick's RC Comprehensive School

APPLE

In the garden you can see
Sitting on the apple tree
Crunchy, round and very sweet
Is the apple that we eat
Red on the top and inside white
Juicy when you take a bite.

Rebecca Quigley (11)
St Patrick's RC Comprehensive School

THE THORNS

The sun caresses the sand like two lover's lust
As it creeps from above the blue, rippling ribbons
The clouds embrace the sky like they're being reunited
The day has just begun.

The tiny humming bird smoothly flies around like it's floating in air,
But the nightingale is nowhere to be seen, although its song is heard
Everything is in deep tranquillity like it's in peaceful slumber.

Slowly but surely the thorns creep in
Entwining themselves among the flower
They're sent on a mission like an army on a day's work
They're sent to destroy, they will if they can.

But as the day comes to an end
The sea, silent and still;
And the sky turns pink like a rose on a winter's day
The thorns wither away like a dying flower
Until the next day comes
Where they will once again choke the beauty of the forest.

Claire Horner (15)
St Patrick's RC Comprehensive School

DYSLEXIA

Feels do you what know it dyslexia have to?
Up fumbled words
Your its problem not
Can't you help?
Understand others don't
Not why?
Day they one experience might it themselves.

Jennie McPhee (11)
St Patrick's RC Comprehensive School

THE JOURNEY

I watched her standing on the crumbling cliff
Her auburn hair glowing in the sun's last light.
Her dark eyes gazed intently out onto the vast ocean.
As the light dimmed she became more despondent.
I followed her petite figure as she began her gradual descent.
Along the old dock and past the harbour, she loitered.
The mood was tense, even the breeze appeared to be aware,
Of the sombre situation, as it rustled in appropriate spaces.
I heard the fishermen murmuring their goodbyes,
As they hurried home for their suppers.
She began strenuously clambering upon a weather-beaten rock,
And there she sat.
As the dusk settled, she began her melancholy cry.
The sorrowful harmony was carried by the wind,
And it floated gently out to sea.
The melodic tune aroused the deep.
In a ceremonious fashion, fins could be seen among the waves
Mauves, azure's, russets and lemons all danced joyfully.
Their colours blending like a kaleidoscope.
Then a gentle laugh rippled the waters.
The beautiful maiden on the rock stared tearfully at the spectrum.
As she reminisced of happier times.
She looked exasperated!
However, the show continued.
Music rang out from the seabed and more creatures joined the choir.
At last however the show ended.
The sea began to calm
And the lights began to shine.
The morning rays of the sun made the water glisten serenely
And the seabirds began to awaken.
Once again she began to journey to her home on the cliff.
For because of past foolishness, the mermaid was forced
To remain human for the rest of her days.

Jenny Macaulay (15)
St Patrick's RC Comprehensive School

HUMAN EFFICIENCY SYNDROME

Here
A mint condition body you can use
Abuse
In any way that you see fit
That's it.
An all-inclusive face plus nose
Ten toes
Packed neatly on your feet
Complete.

Look at you. How versatile. Unique.
No freak
Like those 'handicapped' that we exclude
Quite crude
When equal rights still wobble on the brink.
I think
They crave those gifts you waste each day
The way
You ridicule and vandalise
Surprise!
There's only so much time before you're dead.
Instead.

Train up your tools, perfect the arts
It smarts;
I know. But in the end you'll see
Trust me
Go on - fight for that winning score
What for?
To mess the minds of those who don't want skill
Don't fret
They will.

Daniel Kelly (16)
St Patrick's RC Comprehensive School

A SUMMER'S DAY

At the beach on a summer's day
people getting hit by a sunray
children buying cold ice creams
running around with merry screams
people paddling
children laughing with glee
boat on the smooth water
as far as the eye can see.

People flying soaring kites
walking past amusements with seductive lights
sweet smelling aromas flashing from the shops
when will the money spending ever stop?
As the night clouds form,
it brings along a mid-summer's storm.

The end to all the fun.

Brett Spence (13)
St Patrick's RC Comprehensive School

FOOTBALL

My team
walked onto
the pitch. All of the
team were rich.
The team kicks off
they pass the
ball. We score a
goal in the back
of the net.
We're top of
the league.

Daniel O'Riordan (11)
St Patrick's RC Comprehensive School

AUTUMN

The golden crisp leaves fall from the trees
And scatter all over the ground
The small woodland creatures are hibernating
And shiny conkers like tennis balls fall all around.

Autumn is near
Autumn is here
Autumn is coming now.

The leaves rustle like paper in the whistling wind
And the birds sing sweetly like a lullaby in your dream.
I love autumn
It's my favourite season,
I wish it would come every week.

Rachael Postgate (11)
St Patrick's RC Comprehensive School

SNIPER WOLF

Watching, waiting not moving a muscle,
For hours, days, it didn't matter.
The air was dense, full of fear.
She smelt it like a young child smells chocolate.
It drew her closer, her hunger growing stronger.
Silent, all alone stalking her prey.
Out of the darkness of the shadows she saw the prey move,
Slinking around as if she was a cat, she moved forward.
A red dot, the death mark for many,
Strikes the target right between the eyes.
She smiles evilly to herself,
Because that's one down and two to go.

Jennifer Heatley (14)
St Patrick's RC Comprehensive School

BLUE

Refreshing, clear skies, a bright summer's day,
Soothing sea waters, peaceful cool winds.
Contentment, harmony, joyous thoughts, full emotions,
Captivating nature, where calm feelings play.

Contrasting tones . . . dark, faint and bright,
Moonlit lakes, strokes of soft, whispering light.
Generosity, wisdom, collected . . . yet strong,
Enchanting, tranquil tides, placid silence once gone.

Crystalline icicles hanging . . . so composed . . . so limpid,
Immaculate droplets, shimmering, luminous, free.
Trust, love echoing, smiling, patience,
Chilling, smooth visions . . . so hopeful, mild . . . serene.

Dolphins and sea sharks, torsos so precious,
Beneath eerie depths . . . composed though somewhat vicious.
Cloudless evening sunsets, shattered shining glass,
Dinky dragonflies dazzling, while tranquil hours pass.

Tumbling rain globules, descending, transparent, mild,
Pristine puddle splashes, seeking an infuriated child.
Moonbeams reflection, shimmering streams,
Dappling dew upon limp, autumn leaves.
Deserted, damp yard, a juvenile daughter grieves.
Secretive scenery, shattered youthful dreams.

Melodious memories, gentle northerly breeze,
Tender, tuneful wind chimes, sweet sea fish, sedate.
Mysterious, precious nature, soothing, clam . . . at ease,
Tears like winter droplets . . . merciful, hatred, fate

Whistling winter gales, compassionate beliefs,
Hidden harmonies, sinking, forgotten fantasies come true.
Endless phrases spring to mind . . . the dappled, drifting leaves,
Whenever this extraordinary shade is visualised . . .
The miraculous colour blue.

Rachel Kelly (14)
St Patrick's RC Comprehensive School

THE WINTER SKY

The winter snow is gleaming
The summer sun has left
Some people could be dreaming
About the presents they're going to get.

Winter, winter, winter star
I don't know where you are
Like a ball, like a flying star.

The winter moon is shining
The children anxiously miming
The Christmas lights are chiming
The stars seem like they're rhyming.

Winter, winter, winter star
I don't know where you are
Like a ball, like a flying star.

The winter stars are blinding
The moon is really shining
Flying stars are rhyming
Then the moon will mime.

Winter, winter, winter star
I don't know where you are
Like a ball, like a flying star.

Christopher Raymond (11)
St Patrick's RC Comprehensive School

LIFE

Open thoughts throughout your mind,
Closed feelings you leave behind,
Each breath is a silent moment
Searching for a dream you may never find.

Time flashes by, stretching its long span
Each separate second sounded by the Tambourine Man
The hours fly past, the pendulum swinging,
The strongest times announced by the chime bells ringing.

Good feelings released through an open door,
But harsh hurts itch beneath the skin.
The darkness of aching as your body shuts down,
A new day born, eyes open, light in.

What we call our destiny is never real,
But a hope hidden behind a dream.
We await our fortune, given in time,
Another day, another sign.

When will it come, we count the days,
The hours the minutes, we will await.
Until that time, until the end,
It matters no more it *will* end.

How it goes, we are unsure
The silent moments creep,
Fewer and fewer.

The light fades, the feelings slide
Down that pathway, it all does glide
Through the tunnels of pain and strife
The dreaded journey they do call 'life.'

Beverley Marwood (15)
St Patrick's RC Comprehensive School

THE MATCH

So much optimism in the morning
Getting all fired up to go
Wanting to see excitement
Wanting a victory
You take your seat
It begins.
On the attack
Feeling your heart pump
He shoots, he scores!
You jump up and go crazy
Great start!
Now you're on the defence
Feeling nervous, please miss
The equaliser!
You put your hands over your face
Half-time
Eating a pie.
Kick-off again, willing your team to score,
Come on! Come on!
Shots are being fired in, but they all miss
Injury time
Last minute winner!
We won!
You leave the stadium in delight
To go dancing in the streets,
But suddenly you wake up
Noooo!
It was just a dream.

Martin Heward (13)
St Patrick's RC Comprehensive School

MY MIND

My dreams and ideas
swirling around like an endless
black hole
lost in a vacuum of time and space.

Ambitions and thoughts roaming around
as if they've been set in
stone for life.

Questions are caged animals
alert and ready to pounce on anything
resembling an answer.

What, will, why, when, daydreaming
about what troubles and fascinates
me
the distant past and the futuristic
future.

My mind is what I'm writing about
could it be a galaxy?
Stars are my thoughts, a plant my brain.

My staring into space will have to
come to a sudden stop
the teachers going ape pacing the
classroom
expecting an answer, but
he'll have to wait my caged
animal hasn't caught
one yet.

Steven Liggett (13)
St Patrick's RC Comprehensive School

THE BELL

Tick-tock
Will the bell ever go?

Tick-tock
Will we get to play in the snow?

Tick-tock
Hurry up bell and ring

Tick-tock
I want to play with my dog King

Tick-tock
Homework, Yuck!

Tick-tock
I just want to play in the muck!

Tick-tock
Ten seconds to go

Tick-tock

Hurry up bell
Go! Go! Go!

Tick-tock
Brrriinnggg!

Yeah!

Kathryn Buckland (12)
St Patrick's RC Comprehensive School

THE DAZZLING DAY AT THE BEACH

One sunny summer day
I met my friend Mai
We together went for a swim
And then along came Kim.

I listened to the sea crashing
And watched the sun glistening
I started sizzling
Then the sea started bashing.

The wind was whistling
As we were listening
The sand blew
As the birds flew.

Then the air calmed down
And I turned brown
At the end of the day
Me and my friend Mai went home.

Sammi Brocardo (11)
St Patrick's RC Comprehensive School

GRANNY

Granny used to be normal, as far as I can tell,
But now she runs all over town causing havoc and hell.
She used to hobble down to school, it was like an hour long hike,
But now she turns up just in time, perched upon a motorbike!

Granny used to be normal, as far as I can say,
But she seems to be growing worse, with every passing day.
She used to sit and knit or have her little naps,
But now she's wearing tracksuits and branded baseball caps.

Granny used to be normal, or so I seemed to think
Now she's wearing bloomers, striped with green and pink!
Even though she's odd and often seems astray
To me she seems so perfect in every other way!

Richaela Smith (13)
St Patrick's RC Comprehensive School

WINTER

Cold, snow, sleet and rain,
Dark, grey mornings day after day,
Sleep in,
Late for school,
Fight for the bathroom,
'Dad let's go.'
Scrape off the snow
And clear the windows,
Get to school just in time,
Everyone is miserable,
Because of the
Snow, sleet and rain.

Cold, snow, sleet and rain
Home from school it's just the same.
In front of the fire,
Curl up in a ball,
Nice and warm.
Get ready for bed,
Big, fluffy pyjamas,
Hop into bed where it's toasty and warm.
But outside the
Cold, snow, sleet and rain
Carries on without me.

Samantha Pearce (14)
St Patrick's RC Comprehensive School

WINTERTIME

The roar of the ocean
It is wintertime and I've made the potion
We put on our gloves and our hats
We hope we don't see any more rats.
We walk to the shops to get the decorations
While people get ready for the Christmas celebration
Watching the snow
Hit the floor at our white, frosty door.
Making the snowman, big and bold
With all the snow that's icy cold.
It's Christmas Day and we're opening our presents
So my mum opens her presents
And finds out it's a dog
So she gives it a hug
And calls it Bud.
It's coming in dark
My mum says goodnight
I go upstairs
And she turns out the light.
The angel glows on the tree
Lights all shining at me
And all twinkling in rows
Even the sparkly red bows
Is it over?
I am covered up in my cover.

Michaela Gale (11)
St Patrick's RC Comprehensive School

THE WAY SHE MAKES ME SMILE

I like a girl with big, greeny-blue eyes
It reminds me of the ocean.
Her long blonde hair glistens like the sand
And her big, beautiful smile makes me smile too.

Her delicate body moves like the wind
When her little hands touch me I get butterflies
And I chill up my spine,
But all in all every day I see her
Nothing matters, but how much I love her.

Kane Garry-Madden (13)
St Patrick's RC Comprehensive School

EDUCATION

I know you think education is sad,
But come on it seriously isn't that bad.
Without it you wouldn't be accepted for any job,
And you will definitely end up a lazy slob.

It's sad to say to, but if you look at education as a joke,
Do you realise that you will end up broke?
Playing the class fool and acting funny,
Won't bring you a career full of prospects and money.

If you pass your exams and complete your work,
You will be the one rewarded with many perks.
Lot's of money, a luxurious car
Many holidays, exotic and far.

People have made education sound glum,
But I'll tell you something it's great fun.
If you work as hard as you like to play,
You will be successful in every way.

When you look upon the horizon and study your life,
You will be glad you weren't the one who caused trouble and strife.
Schooling has shown you your talents and gave you every opportunity,
To realise that life and education join together in unity.

Sarah Barron (16)
St Patrick's RC Comprehensive School

WINTER

The nights are getting darker,
The coldness is surrounding me,
My woolly hat, scarf and gloves come out of the drawers,
Animals are hibernating,
Winter is coming.

The children chatter,
Their breath blowing like smoke in the air,
The gardens become bland, flowers wilt and die,
Chuck, chucker, a car won't start,
Curtains drawn, children inside,
Winter is near.

The snow is falling, winter is near,
I can hear snowdrops drip, drip, dripping,
The trees are covered, like icing on a cake,
Everybody's gardens look the same,
Winter is here.

Children are skating on the ice, they are excited,
Windows are dressed with flashing lights,
Everyone is dashing, jolly in the snow,
Carols bellowing from all around,
Winter is now.

Abigail Smith (12)
St Patrick's RC Comprehensive School

SISTER

Each day I wake
The few steps I take
To the open doors
The day once more begins with gloom
As my sister has beaten me to the bathroom.

Mother's glare as we come downstairs
My sister, gross as she eats her toast
She takes a sip, but slurps her tea
Oh for pity's sake
Help me.

Neil Young (12)
St Patrick's RC Comprehensive School

THE GREAT WHITE

Swiftly it moves, but not too fast,
Piercing the water like a knife.
All its learning from the past
Stays with it through all its life.

Now the radar signal's working,
And has some prey in its sight.
Like a submarine a lurking,
It flashes past to have a bite.

He gets the leg, the prey moves back
The prey knows now that he is here.
Speed and cunning he does not lack,
The prey doesn't know just what to fear.

He rises from the deep, dark bottom,
Now he's nearly at the top.
He tears the flesh as though it's cotton,
The man was there and now he's not.

Swiftly it moves, but not too fast,
Piercing the water like a knife.
His bellyache has gone at last,
He's now living a fuller life.

Stephen Carter (13)
St Patrick's RC Comprehensive School

WINTER

When winter comes
we shout for joy
we all get presents
girls and boys.

When winter comes
we go out to play
we build our snowmen
that melt that day.

When winter comes
we are all ice-cold
we wrap in blankets
and fold and fold.

When winter comes
we are filled with love
we stare at the tree
and at the great white dove.

Chelsea Hobson (11)
St Patrick's RC Comprehensive School

SPORTS

Football, cricket we have the lot
My opinion is - sports rule!
Gymnastics - I think not
You know the bleep test, it is so cool.

Badminton, rock climbing, we have the lot
Scoring goals, batting a ball
I like football more than a lot
Jogging and jogging until we fall.

Heart rate, flexibility we have the lot
For a tall lad I am quite fit
I liked PE in my cot
Have you seen my footie kit?

Shaun Liggett (12)
St Patrick's RC Comprehensive School

SILHOUETTE IN THE SKY

The sky is blue
The tide is out
The sand is golden
Without a doubt.

People waiting to meet you
The shields are up
The towels are out
They can't wait to see you about.

The clouds move away
They see you
With your bright sparkle
In the summer blue
Everyone is out
Just to meet you.

The day is ending
Time to say 'Bye'
The people leave the golden sand.

You leave the sky
With your burning ache,
Just to think you're out tomorrow.

Peter Roscoe (15)
St Patrick's RC Comprehensive School

SILENT FRIEND

Every day,
my silent friend,
listens to me.
Helps me to express my feelings.
Never laughs or ridicules me,
never argues or falls out with me.

Every day,
my silent friend
listens to me.
It's a shoulder to cry on,
when I'm feeling down.
When I'm feeling lonely.

Every day,
my silent friend,
listens to me.
My best friend.
My silent friend.
My diary.

Rosemary Hare (14)
St Patrick's RC Comprehensive School

FEAR IN THE NIGHT

The house was dark,
No one in sight.
A creak in the floorboards,
Gave me a fright.

A scurry and scrape,
The house begins to settle.
The atmosphere feels make-believe,
Like the story of Hansel and Gretel.

The door opens,
A shadow appears.
Now I realise,
It was only my fears.

Joanne Smith (14)
St Patrick's RC Comprehensive

FOOTBALL

Football, football in the park
Hopefully I can make my mark
Play in goal for Liverpool
Get it right and I'll be cool.

Safest hands in Thornaby
First my town, then my country
My only wish is to be the best
Remember me, forget the rest.

Number one, first man out,
Always the one to scream and shout
Wonderful catches, saves and dives
I always put the game in revive.

Playing wherever I find a field
Hopefully I can get a sign-on deal
Get a slap-up after match meal
Score the goal that sets the seal.

Football, football in the park
Hopefully I can make my mark
Play in goal for Liverpool
Get it right and I'll be cool.

Daniel Booth (12)
St Patrick's RC Comprehensive School

SEPTEMBER 11TH

There they stood
So tall and strong
Until one day it all went wrong
The planes came down
In they were sent
Down to the ground the towers went
Together they stood
Divided they fell
It was like a living hell
As the thick, black smoke engulfed the city
As day turned to night
We pray for those who have lost
People they love
This is too big a cost
They left their loved ones behind
To all those heroes who went so kind
We won't forget, we won't let die
All the memories of those who died
September 11th will remain
So will the memories of the heroes God has gained
As we rebuild the world in love and hope
We pray to God so we can cope
Nations pull together
To beat this terror
We won't lie low, we won't hide away
The world will come together again one day.

Marianne Bishara (13)
St Patrick's RC Comprehensive School

STRANGE ANIMALS

Billy the rat,
He's big and smelly,
He's so big,
He ate a welly.

Carrie the cat,
Went astray,
Where she went,
She couldn't say.

Barry the bat,
Lost his wings,
Barry the bat,
Now instead he sings.

All of these animals
Are really strange
So if you see them
Take fire at range.

Jamie Fraser (11)
St Patrick's RC Comprehensive School

BEAST

Beast, beast from the north east
he prowls in the night
he is scared of the light.
He runs through the centre with a sausage roll
the fat thing - his mam, is on the dole.

Daniel Nicholson (13)
St Patrick's RC Comprehensive School

MY SCHOOL GOAL

Floor, swallow my teachers whole
As then I've reached my school goal
With a puppy dog's tail,
    Bat's wing,
    Frog's leg,
    Cat's eye,
    Body of devil,
    Fish bone,
    Let's go!
Now I'm higher than all the rest
So please get rid of the school pest
Again with a puppy dog's tail,
    Bat's wing,
    Frog's leg,
    Cat's eye,
    Body of devil,
    Fish bone,
    It's done!

Natalie Brooks (11)
St Patrick's RC Comprehensive School

BIRTHDAYS

B   rilliant presents
I   rresistible chocolates
R   ooms full of people eating cake
T   hirsty adults drinking wine
H   appy birthday we all sing
D   aydreaming about all the money you got
A   rranging the decorations
Y   oung children playing with party poppers
S   leeping well on the night.

Elizabeth Harrison (13)
St Patrick's RC Comprehensive School

FRIGHT IN THE NIGHT

Nobody knew they'd get a fright
In the night.
As the wind howled
And monstrous animals prowled.
In the house
There was a squeak from a mouse
The wind then grumbled,
And the house rumbled.
There was a spark of lightning
That was rather frightening.
The floor creaked
And the taps leaked.
All of a sudden a white shape revealed,
The only problem was, its face was concealed.
It looked like it was enclosed under a hat,
Its feet didn't even make contact with the mat.
Nobody could escape the torment of the house,
Or the squeak from the mouse!

Charlotte Riley (13)
St Patrick's RC Comprehensive School

FOOTBALL

F   un is football
O   n side
O   ffside
T   hrow ins
B   alls out, balls in the back of the net
A   warded free kicks, goal kicks, corner kicks
L   ines all around
L   ife is football!

Paul Thompson (12)
St Patrick's RC Comprehensive School

BIRTHDAYS

B irthdays are fun
I ndoors and outdoors
R acing around the dance floor!
T eenagers acting cool
H elping themselves to the party food
D ancing and playing party games
A lways having fun
Y ear after year we celebrate using lots of silly string.

Laura Maleary (13)
St Patrick's RC Comprehensive School

AMERICA

F un both day and night,
L aughter and sun 24/7,
O rlando's the best place to be,
R ides and attractions for everyone to see
I nternational Drive, shops and diners for you,
D isney has fun and attractions too,
A merica the best place to be for you.

Andrew Pearce (13)
St Patrick's RC Comprehensive School

GINGER

G inger is the colour of my hair
I nteresting to look at
N ice, shiny, long and curly
G lowing in the sunlight
E ven good enough to eat
R eally you should see it, it would be a treat!

Abi Leck (11)
St Patrick's RC Comprehensive School

RAINBOWS

R ed is for anger, hatred and power.
A pricot is for peace and harmony.
I ndigo is for life and friendships.
N avy is for cold, misty times.
B lack is for moods, dark times.
O range is for kindness and sunsets.
W hite is for love and happiness.
S imon you're with us always, shining over us all the time.

Stephen O'Hara (13)
St Patrick's RC Comprehensive School

BECKHAM

B rilliant Beckham
E xpert at free kicks
C lass captain
K icks it in the net
H ungry for goals
A nd he is . . .
M int!

Jack Taylor (12)
St Patrick's RC Comprehensive School

FOOTBALL

Speeding up the field
Controlling the ball
Dodging through the gaps
When I get the chance
I take a great shot
Wow! It's a goal!

William Cheng (13)
St Patrick's RC Comprehensive School

SCAREDY-CAT

I know a man who was scared,
Scared of the dark,
But only because he was dared,
To sleep in a haunted park.
The night was as cold as ice,
And pitch-black,
He seen several hundred mice,
Which nearly gave him a heart attack.
He thought he was gong to die,
So he hid behind a fence.
But it was only a woman walking by,
But he was still pretty tense.
He was shivering like a leaf,
When he heard a strange sound.
But it was only his false teeth,
Rattling on the ground.
So now our man faced his fear,
And told his mates the story.
He bought them all a beer,
And basked in all his glory.

Paul Suckling (15)
St Patrick's RC Comprehensive School

THE WICKED WITCH

The Wicked Witch of the North is dead
She lies deep down in her ice-cold bed
Her wicked deeds will be no more
Since Dorothy melted her into the floor
This pleased the people all around
The witch can no longer be found.

James Grimley (14)
St Patrick's RC Comprehensive School

DAY AND NIGHT

Night flew over with his long, dark cape,
The stars whizzed up to meet him.
The moon was their leader and they all bow
Down to him their master.
The stream played the music
'Trickle, trickle' it played.
The stars sang 'Twinkle, twinkle'
The breeze danced and twirled,
The dancing went on all night.

Suddenly light flew in and broke up the party
And sent away the night
The stream sparkled brightly
The stars and moon just disappeared
The trees all waved and the sun smiled
Her own motherly smile,
But the peace of nature has all gone
For people are in sight.

Sarah Johnson (11)
St Patrick's RC Comprehensive School

DARKNESS IS . . .

Darkness is evil,
Darkness is war,
Darkness is scary and so much more,
Darkness is blood,
Darkness is in the mind,
Darkness is something you should not find.
Darkness is here,
Darkness is there,
Darkness is something which has no lair.

Sean Gibson (13)
St Patrick's RC Comprehensive School

FORMULA 1 - FAST AND FURIOUS

Fast and furious they zoom along
Into the pits they're so quick
Back out in a flick
Over the finish line they're so quick.

Monaco is coming, prepare to qualify
Or you'll end up in a pile.

Schumacher first, Montoya second
They're so quick you'll never catch it.

The chequered flag is waiting near the finishing line
Fast and furious like a fly.

The race is over and the track is warm
Golden glory, I'm standing tall.

Ashley Simpson (13)
St Patrick's RC Comprehensive School

THE AMERICAN DISASTER

On the 11th of September
That day I'll always remember
The terrorists hijacked four planes
Which caused a lot of pain.
Thousands of people died
Not many survived
The special armed forces were sent in,
But there was no sign of him.
The Americans attacked some Afghanistan air bases
And now there are some anthrax cases.

Joe Vipond (13)
St Patrick's RC Comprehensive School

SUMMERTIME

I wake up to the beaming sun
Circular and bright like a ripe, fresh orange
The waves rippling against the shore
Like a never-ending whirlpool.
The sand under my feet, itching and sore
Like a furnace beneath my feet
As it slips beneath my wet toes.
The sun starts to burn my back
All I want to do is get into the water
Still and silent, as the day closes to an end
I can see the reflection of the hotels on the sea
The rest of the sea is dark, tranquil
Like a huge sapphire blanket covering over it.
The shops start to close and so do the pubs,
Silent . . .
It is now time to go to sleep and get ready
For a fun-filled day tomorrow.

Melissa Smith (16)
St Patrick's RC Comprehensive School

THE LION

Hiding, watching, listening, not moving
sitting ready to pounce at any moment.

The bending of knees as quiet as a
mouse, ready to strike.
So next time you're in the
jungle you had better watch out
you don't know who's watching you . . .

Daniel McBride (12)
St Patrick's RC Comprehensive School

DADDY

Daddy, why do people die?
And Daddy, when they do why do we cry?

Daddy, where do babies come from?
Daddy, do birds really bring them from the sun?

Daddy, why is the grass green?
Daddy, does the rain keep it clean?

Daddy, why are you bigger than me?
Daddy, why aren't you as big as a tree?

Daddy, what's the difference between girls and boys?
Daddy, why do we play with different toys?

Daddy . . .

Hannah Flewker (13)
St Patrick's RC Comprehensive School

EARTH

It is dark and black
Nothing is there
Until one day a huge ball came by
It burst with a *bang*!
And then there is life
Balls fly by
All different colours
The balls are hard apart from which there is life.
It is green and blue,
But inside it is colourful
Smell of fresh trees and grass
It is full of life!

Kevin Cheng (11)
St Patrick's RC Comprehensive School

HELP I'M A BULLY!

Help I'm a bully and everyone's afraid.
I let my guilt be the master, I hate what has been made!
I go home, my mother's drunk on the floor,
I run upstairs, I can't take it anymore!
When I reach school every day
My torment takes over, I punch my fears away!
Then I am in trouble, I do honestly care, because
Wherever I walk, kids shiver with scares!
I've ruined my life is all I can say
Because since five years old I forgot how to play!
With my mother a devoted smoker,
My father a gambler and a loner!
Then it's me the bully, alone in the world
My life so dark, twisted like curls.
I think I shall end with a short goodbye
Maybe I hope one day my time will come
When I shall fly!

Elizabeth Dickinson (12)
St Patrick's RC Comprehensive School

USA STRIKES BACK

Orange and yellow explosives light up
the still, black night.
The roar and thunder of USA planes as they burst out across the
undisturbed sky disturbing the quiet towns of Afghanistan.
The cry of people as they slither around the rumble and dust looking for
their family or belongings like snakes looking for food.
As this occurs Osama bin Laden is hiding, running, trembling at the
force and domination of the USA military.
One man's hate for a nation.

Darren Trainer (15)
St Patrick's RC Comprehensive School

I WENT TO THE PICTURES

I went to the pictures tomorrow
I got a front seat at the back
A woman gave me a packet of biscuits
I ate them and gave her them back.
It was nothing to get in
So I paid at the door
There was plenty of seats, but I sat on the floor.

I went to the match next Saturday
I got a back seat at the front
I bought a packet of crisps
Ate them and gave them back.
It was six pounds to get in
So I paid twelve pounds at the exit.
There was plenty of seats, but I sat on the roof.

Glen Butterworth (11)
St Patrick's RC Comprehensive School

MY FRIENDS

Jessica is really quiet and shy,
sometimes you think you'll make her cry.
Chelsea is always there,
when we're together we make a right pair.
Holly is jolly, she's always got news
whatever she does she doesn't want to lose.
Kayleigh is loud and always proud.
Natalie is fun she is really good when she runs.
Zara is tall unlike Laura who is really small.
Sammy likes, cats but hates rats.
They are my friends, no one said they were perfect.

Kerry Nolan (11)
St Patrick's RC Comprehensive School

WAR

The explosion of bombs on a dark night
The screams of terror, agony and fright
The sound of soldiers marching to battle
People being slaughtered just like mindless cattle.
The sound of bullets tearing through flesh
Why is this world in such a mess?
No child should go through this or adult too
Does no one care about what they do?
No one should go through this much pain
So why do they do it, what's there to gain?
Except the loss of innocent lives
Of adults, children, husbands and wives
People left homeless, out on the street
With nowhere to live and nothing to eat
So what is the point in all this war
When all it does is destroy us all?

Charlotte Green (12)
St Patrick's RC Comprehensive School

SCHOOL MEALS! YUCK!

Narrator: You're sitting in your classroom, watching the clock tick.
Me: If you think I'm waiting for my dinner you must be thick.
Narrator: The clock strikes 12:30, you grab your stuff and leave.
Me: There had better be a different menu! I hate ham and cheese
Narrator: You take a peep through the kitchen door.
Me: There doesn't seem to be much in store.
Narrator: Inside the dinner hall you stand in line.
Me: I must admit the smell is divine!
Narrator: But you gulp at what you see . . .
Me: Oh no . . . spaghetti!

Georgina James (11)
St Patrick's RC Comprehensive School

GILLY

Gilly you were a kind man,
I think you were a Boro fan.
You were a wee Scottish fellow,
You weren't a pest you were always the best.

Gilly why, why, why did you have to go?
To that work in the sky,
Oh you didn't have to die
I wish it were a lie.

You never thought of dying
You never told a lie.
You wouldn't have to take the test to get into heaven
You were already booked into room number seven.

Scott Wilson (13)
St Patrick's RC Comprehensive School

CHILDREN

Crying, lying little children,
How can parents have them?
Changing smelly nappies
And crying through the night!

They want to have more freedom,
They weren't like this when they were young.
Sometimes parents feel they can kill them!

When they leave home,
They have a place of their own
They cry down the phone,
Wishing they were back home!

Hope Kemp (12)
St Patrick's RC Comprehensive School

SONNET

Wandering around, just a lost soul,
No friends, no family, no school, no home,
His clothes are all torn, his jeans have a hole
He ignores all the rules and just wants to roam.
His past is a bleak tale, his upbringing poor.
His mum enjoyed a smoke and drink now and again
His childhood taught him that heartbreak had no cure.
His brother was a minor and loved causing pain.
Filled with neglect is this boy's story
No one in his world to show him compassion,
But through all this hate came a figure of glory,
A bird of great beauty in a unique and proud fashion
The bird was his only possession
An object of love in a world full of hate.

Kathryn O'Hara (15)
St Patrick's RC Comprehensive School

IMAGINE . . .

Imagine if you were a fish in the sea
You wouldn't be like a squirrel because he lives in a tree.
Imagine if you were a cat playing with yarns of wool
It would be nothing like being a donkey because his life is dull.
Imagine if you were a sheep lying in a field
You'd be just like a dog tied up on a lead.
Imagine if you were a panda with your fur black and white
You'd be similar to a zebra except from the height.
Imagine if you were a giraffe standing high and proud
You would be nothing like a hyena - Ow! they're loud.
Imagine if you were an adult when life's not always a thrill
You'd be nothing like me because my life is brill.

Raychael Speight (14)
St Patrick's RC Comprehensive School

TIME

It creeps around corners,
Without you knowing.
It will smother you with creases,
Never slowing, until the end, ongoing.

You always need more,
But you in no way compare,
It has nothing to do with you,
You just wait around in despair.

Its rhythm never faults,
The forever tick-tick-tick-tick,
Waiting for it to overtake us,
For it to take its toll.

Marise Barclay (15)
St Patrick's RC Comprehensive School

HOLIDAYS

You're as brown as a berry
As pink as a lobster
Lying on the beach under a big yellow monster!

Slap on your suncream
Till you're as white as a sheet
Splash in the pool and go out to eat!

Back on the aeroplane
The sunny heaven ends
Still, you can't wait to see your friends!

Kate Hare (11)
St Patrick's RC Comprehensive School

BOARDING

Standing at the top
of the ramp like
snow on a mountain,
shivering until the
point where you pick
up the courage to
push off. The time has
come. Bang you've hit
the bottom like a
stampede of elephants.
Seconds
seemed to last
forever as you approached
the next ramp, like a
tiger sprinting, diving to
catch its prey.

Dominic Brown (12)
St Patrick's RC Comprehensive School

PEOPLE

There are some nasty people in the world.
Why don't we all be friends?
Everyone can be angry
Can you be?
Yes, you can
Try not to be and try to be kind to me.
There are some people in the world
Who are very kind.
All the very nasty people should be hanging on the line.

Daniel Brown (11)
St Patrick's RC Comprehensive School

FOOTBALL

I think football is good,
Even though there's usually some blood.
I lean on the edge of my seat,
Wondering whether we're going to get beat.
I sometimes start singing,
Especially if my team's winning.
I maybe put a bet on,
If Boro's playing Bolton.
I sometimes watch it in the pub,
Or in the local club.
I enjoy watching Beckham's free kicks,
They're so good I often wonder if it's a fix.
I like watching Brazil,
They always seem kings of the hill.
Football is the best,
Better than the rest.

Chris Casson (13)
St Patrick's RC Comprehensive School

HIS LOVE I'LL NEVER GAIN!

Love is a chain around my heart,
nothing can tear it or break it apart.
No matter what I do, it won't go away,
so I live to fight it another day,
and resist the temptation to approach you this day.

The love I feel is kept inside,
in a safe place where it can hide.
But when I saw you out it came,
from the tattoo in my heart inscribed with your name.

Jay McNichol (13)
St Patrick's RC Comprehensive School

AS I LOOK

As I look up into the sky,
I see the never-ending circular,
shape, smiling down at me!
Shining so bright, giving
the world a tint of light.

As I look up at the world,
I see them winking at me!
With their own personality
and their own place reserved
on the mass of darkness.

As I look up at the sky,
I see the misty, mysterious clouds.
They move around and about in
many ways, while passing
the world by without care.

Nerissa Stewart (15)
St Patrick's RC Comprehensive School

WAR

When will war start?
Two planes get hijacked
They flew into the Twin Towers and the Pentagon
The rescuers hurry to help the injured
War starts.
The Americans go off to Afghanistan
The Americans start shooting trying to get Bin Laden.

Ian Parnaby (11)
St Patrick's RC Comprehensive School

STORM

The sky was turning black,
The clouds were vastly expanding.
Blocking all traces of sunlight,
As if it was banished from the Earth.

Within seconds the rain was trickling,
Within minutes it began to pound.
Followed by the first crash of thunder
A breathtaking sound.

Forks of lightening,
Plunging down through the clouds,
Rarely piercing the face of the Earth,
Blinding the eyes of the stunned spectators.

Now the destructive monster,
Has given up and moved on.
Silence has been left behind him,
The storm has gone.

Anna Rees (15)
St Patrick's RC Comprehensive School

HE'S IN EVERYTHING

He's in the rain that falls,
He's in the wind that blows.
He's in the rainbow that crosses the sky
He's in the fallen leaves that pass us by.

He's in the grass that grows,
He's in the trees that bloom.
He's in the seasons that came,
My dear brother who's gone.

Ruth Paterson (13)
St Patrick's RC Comprehensive School

AUTUMN

As the leaves fall and crumple on the ground
I love to hear the rustling sound
As the branches sway with the breeze
The raindrops fall off the trees
Autumn, the season I like the best
As the earth prepares for its winter rest.

Red, yellow, brown and rust
The leaves fall and turn to dust
The wind blows in my face
As I bend down to fasten my lace
Autumn is a season with lots of things
I thank the world for what it brings.

Autumn is my favourite season
Because there are different things to see
I am very grateful for the world
And that's how I think it should be.

Jonathan Rees (11)
St Patrick's RC Comprehensive School

DINOSAUR COMES TO DINNER

As I walked home from school one day,
A dinosaur followed me all the way.
As my mam looked in dismay,
My new friend and I went out to play.

It's dinner time now and this dinosaur's a pain,
He ate mine and my mam's chicken chow mein!
He's thirsty now so he went out into the rain,
He could have asked nicely instead of drinking from a drain!

Kerry Day (13)
St Patrick's RC Comprehensive School

LOVE

It started, a warm gentle breeze in spring
Sending shivers of anticipation up my spine.
Buds of a new love bloomed
And soon a colourful riot of flowers blossomed
Eventually rays of passion beamed down
From the glowing sun overhead,
Brightness seemed it would last for eternity.
Passions became too heated, however
And dark storm clouds began to block the rays.
The sky turned purple with anger
And the heavens opened with floods of emotion
Splattered onto the cold, hard ground.
No sooner had the disastrous storm hit
It gradually drifted further and further away
To some other unsuspecting destination,
Oblivious to the mess and confusion it left behind.

Caroline Fowler (14)
St Patrick's RC Comprehensive School

FEELINGS

Feelings are a funny thing that we feel inside,
Some we have to shout aloud, some we have to hide.
The feelings that I like the best are when I'm happy and glad.
The ones that I don't like are when I'm sad or bad.
Sometimes I am tearful and I have to say I'm sorry.
Sometimes I am frightened and it makes me really worry.
When we go on holiday it makes me so excited,
When we get there in the blazing sun I am very delighted.

Daniel Smith (11)
St Patrick's RC Comprehensive School

SABOTAGE?

This deafening, thunderous bellow of air,
Coiling and twisting around and around,
Twitching trees, watching and waiting,
The path of havoc leading their way.
Whirling, whizzing, straight ahead,
Here it comes.
Branches weaken, heart rate roars,
Ear-splitting, roots snapping,
Hell on Earth.
A missile attack, a nuclear bomb?
But why?
Away it goes, it feels no guilt,
Spinning and spiralling around and around,
Rushing to leave yet another scar,
On a no longer forgiving land.

Louise Robinson (15)
St Patrick's RC Comprehensive School

WINTER

On a bitterly cold day all the
children come out to play.
Playing about in the snow, see
how far can the sledge go.
Making a snowman with a carrot nose
coming in with sodden clothes.
Children slipping about on a frozen
pond looking out on the ice and
beyond, children having a snowball
fight one, two, three, four, throw it
with all your might.

Shaun McNamee (13)
St Patrick's RC Comprehensive School

CRUISING

I'm on the motorway in my silver Porsche
I'm just cruising.
I'm driving, been going for an hour
I'm just cruising.
The soft top's down, the wind's in my hair
I'm just cruising.
The sun glints off the bonnet and into my shades
I'm just cruising.
As I go all my troubles are left behind like all the cars I've passed
I'm just cruising.
I feel clam, relaxed and at ease on the road, there are no problems here
I'm just cruising.
I enter a tunnel and darkness surrounds me, I flick on the lights
They drive back the darkness and stand out like a beacon in the night
I'm just cruising.
The tunnel ends and the sun returns warming the leather interior
I've been going a couple of hours, don't know when I'll stop.
You know why?
I'm just cruising.

Adam Winstone (14)
St Patrick's RC Comprehensive School

FOOTBALL

Football is good.
Too good to miss.
Especially when the ball's in the back of the net.
Ref doing his job, telling them off.
Linesman running up and down.
Lucozade being drunk.
Goal!

Daniel Allison (11)
St Patrick's RC Comprehensive School

WEEKEND

3.30 bell rings loudly,
It's Friday and there is a big rush of people
Heading for the door.
The weekend has come,
No more work for two days.
Lazy morning and late nights
Grins of excitement
What lies ahead?
Fun, laughter, frolics and glee,
Saturday morning packed with amusement and
Enjoyment with friends
The day draws to an end,
Been up, dawn till dusk.
Easy going Sundays
Lounge around till twelve and tasty Sunday dinner
Lazy day of the week
No work, no play
Draws to an end
Who knows what will happen next week?

Jade Godwin (14)
St Patrick's RC Comprehensive School

SUMMER

F   amily is to welcome
A   lways love and attention
M   ums and dads care for you
I   n many different ways they will always look after you
L   oving those special days
Y   our family will be there for you.

Lindsey Nolan (13)
St Patrick's RC Comprehensive School

HALLOWE'EN

Hallowe'en comes and it goes,
Who its celebrated for specifically, no one knows.

The witches and gargoyles walk the streets,
Knocking on doors for trick or treats.

Ghosts, gargoyles and spooks, causing frights,
Deadly howls fill the night!

Witches gathering round the cauldron casting spells,
All sorts of creatures from heaven and hell.

A frog's tail and a bat's wing,
The eye of a bird and a wasp's sting.

These ingredients together combined,
Make the potion these creatures drink for a ride.

They come once a year to enjoy this magical night,
To cause a disturbance and maybe a fright!

Mary-Jo Greenwood (15)
St Patrick's RC Comprehensive School

ANIMAL POEMS

I love fish
Lying in a dish
I also love dogs,
But they sleep like logs
Also small cats
Even if they're fat
Everyone loves cute mice
Because they're nice
After all they're very caring.

Cally Payne (11)
St Patrick's RC Comprehensive School

AT THE BEACH

As I stand on the beach
I feel the sand on my feet
I run around making footprints
As the sand blows swiftly
The sand blows around me.

As I swim out in the sea
As far out as can be
I spot a very big ship
Heading into shore for me.

As I try to swim back
Big waves are following me
As they catch me, under I go
Tossing and turning until I hit the shore.

Samantha Towes (12)
St Patrick's RC Comprehensive School

FIREWORKS

Explosive, electrifying, ear-splitting,
Up into the sky,
Glinting, glittering, gleaming,
Making babies cry.
Soaring, sparkling, scattering,
Lighting up the night,
Chromatic, colourful, crackling,
Red, blue, white.
Finishing off the night with the biggest one,
The colours danced and sang,
Everyone close your ears now
Boom, boom bang!

Jessica McCarrick (14)
St Patrick's RC Comprehensive School

CHRISTMAS IS . . .

Christmas is a time of joy
For every happy girl or boy

Christmas is the cold night air
Following you around everywhere

Christmas is a family time
Eating mince pies and drinking wine

Christmas in your comfy bed
Peacefully awaiting your sleepyhead.

But somewhere around the world
There is an unhappy girl or boy
They don't have any presents to open on the day
Or somewhere warm to stay.

Christina Darragh (13)
St Patrick's RC Comprehensive School

LOST

Your face a distant memory,
Your smile I long to see,
The good times we shared,
The moments when we cared.

Our lives in such a mess,
At times you couldn't care less,
About it we don't talk,
So many times have I wanted to walk.

Away from you, away from this hell,
You say you love me, but how can I tell?

Sophie Legg (15)
St Patrick's RC Comprehensive School

AEROPLANE

Soaring through the clouds and
The dark night sky.
As the gentle summer breeze
Takes me to my destination.

The stars brighten up the sky
As if it were street lights,
Put there for me
To get me to my destination.

My wings are the purest white
The lights like the purest gold
It is now me who lights the sky
To get me to my destination.

Danielle McMurray (15)
St Patrick's RC Comprehensive School

STRAWBERRIES!

Strawberry, oh strawberry
You cute looking thing!

Strawberry, little strawberry
As red as your cheeks

Strawberry, red strawberry
You are the one!

But strawberry, oh strawberry
It's time to say bye-bye

I am going to eat you now
So you are going to die!

Nadia Featherstone (11)
St Patrick's RC Comprehensive School

FREEDOM

Animals in captivity,
captured for us to mock.
Taken away their freedom.
Replaced it with cold shock.

Cages far too small,
restricts in every way,
Cramped and not too clean,
not free to run and play.

Behaviour turns extreme,
pacing up and down.
Unhappy and distressed.
Instead of smiles - a frown.

Why do we cage these animals?
Why do we treat them so?
They are born free, let them run free.
Why not let them go?

Stewart Cooper (13)
Westlands School

FOOTBALL CRAZY

I'm crazy about football.
I support Man U and Hartlepool.
One's good and one's bad.
I think I must be a daft lad.

Paul McCabe (12)
Westlands School

TERRIBLE TRAGEDY

People crying
People dying.
Working all day.
Working all night.
New York, New York.
It was an evil act of terrorism.
Terror, terror.
Who's the man?
I'm the man.
And
We'll find the man.

Craig Cockerill (13)
Westlands School

BIN LADEN

New York, New York
On a working morning
People busy in their Twin Towers
Their world goes dark
Their world goes black
Bin Laden, Bin Laden,
Nasty Bin Laden.

Paul Northmore (12)
Westlands School